254 Days to Impeachment

The Future History of the First Independent President

By J.P. Prag

YOU SET OUT TO TELL AN UNTRUE STORY AND YOU TRY TO
MAKE IT BELIEVABLE, EVEN TO YOURSELF. WHICH CALLS
FOR DETAILS; ANY GOOD LIE DOES.

ANNE TYLER

PRIMARY SEASON

Countdown to Impeachment

*FOR THE FIRST TIME SINCE GEORGE WASHINGTON,
AN INDEPENDENT HAS BEEN ELECTED PRESIDENT OF
THE UNITED STATES*

*A newspaper illustration depicting the order to clear the galleries during
the impeachment trial of Andrew Johnson on May 6, 1868. Original wood
engraving by **JAMES E. TAYLOR**, Public Domain, via Wikimedia Commons.*

Just because the President of the United States is unaffiliated, it does not mean that the rest of the Federal
Government has suddenly given up all of its partisan favor-
itisms, partialities, and biases. What happens when an
idealist sits in the most powerful chair on Earth while an
entire bureaucracy fights to stay relevant?

The new President may only have 254 days to make a point—that the world can be completely changed with a different approach, especially one based on honesty, transparency, and accountability. Those few spins of the Earth on its axis are all the President has between taking the Oath of Office and when the next budget must be approved and executed. Should the administration's efforts fail, the government will shut down.

Following from the outside, the media—with all its various perspectives, viewpoints, and ratings-grabbing agendas—reports on the travails of the new President. Everyone has their own story to weave for any-and-all reasons. Some truly believe that "doing the right thing" is not always the "right thing to do", and there are severe consequences that must be paid for even trying. No matter whether intentions are just, there must be a fallout.

Despite this, the President is undeterred. Or at least that is what the leader of the free world is projecting. Should there be doubts and recriminations, it will never be known because no one can get inside the President's head. One thing is clear, though: the President is willing to put the entirety of the United States of America at risk. From Inauguration Day on January 20th to the end of the Fiscal Year on September 30th, the President uses the power of the bully pulpit to its fullest. Yet, because of this, the dust never has time to settle.

When the country reaches that 254-day mark and a standoff ensues, the question simply becomes: can a new way of doing politics truly supplant the entrenched system? Or will the system get its way and remove this President for good?

Table of Contents

FROM YOUR #1 TRUSTED NEWS SOURCE!

Future History or Past Prologue?

A MESSAGE FROM THE AUTHOR

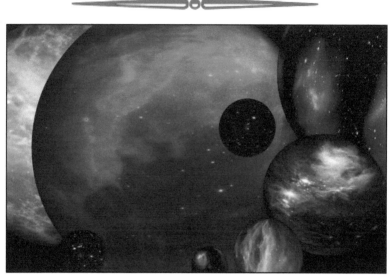

Image by **SILVER SPOON**, CC0, via Wikimedia Commons.

Please note that this novel was essentially completed by mid-October 2022. As such, a lot of assumptions had to be made about how ongoing current events may resolve after that point. Should anything I have written about comes to fruition, it was not prescience, just supposition. If history unfolds completely differently, well, this is just what happened in the universe in which this story takes place.

Submitted for your approval,

J.P. PRAG
OCTOBER 19, 2022

"It is a true story," the monster said. "Many things that are true feel like a cheat."

From *A Monster Calls* by Patrick Ness

UNEXPECTED INAUGURATION

PRESIDENT DECLARES "PARTY IS OVER", LEAVES AFTER SHOCKING ATTENDEES

CONTROVERSIES AMASSED EVEN BEFORE THE NEW PRESIDENT TOOK THE OATH OF OFFICE, AND THEN BALLOONED IMMEDIATELY AFTERWARDS

*After the new President put a quick end to the expected festivities, workers took down the historic flags that were used in the inauguration ceremony at the United States Capitol Building. Photo by **AOC.GOV**, Public Domain, via Wikimedia Commons.*

January 20th (Washington, D.C.) – While Inauguration Day is usually a festive affair, this one proved to be anything but traditional when the new President of the United States of America started the celebration by declaring that the "party is over".

Of course, the newly installed President did arrive at the highest seat in the land through the most unconventional methods. Inspired by the books **NEW & IMPROVED: THE UNITED STATES OF AMERICA** and **ALWAYS DIVIDED, NEVER UNITED**, the Constitution was amended to eliminate the Electoral College and replace it with a mixed ranked and negative voting system. As a result of these alterations, for the first time since the election of 1848 that brought in Zachary Taylor of the Whig Party, someone not affiliated with either the Democratic or Republican Parties was elected. However, even the Whig Party was considered a major Political Party of its day. Thus, a true comparison would be to the last President who was not affiliated with any dominant Party: George Washington.

That is not to say that this President should be likened to George Washington—at least not yet. Still, based on what happened next, the comparisons are being made by those who support the President the most. Detractors, on the other hand, are already proclaiming vindication by declaring that the President's actions demonstrate what happens when someone with limited political experience and service is given so much power. Whatever the case, the world has already changed irreparably in ways that cannot be easily undone. No part of the government or society will be able to reverse the course this President has now set the country on, no matter the consequences.

Even before assuming office, the new President caused a stir by choices made in the swearing in process. Despite traditions dating back to the aforementioned George Washington, the President refused to be sworn in while placing a hand on the Bible. Citing the First Amendment, the President made it clear that involving a Bible in a secular government procedure would be tantamount to endorsing a religion. While recent Presidents like Donald Trump, Barack Obama, and others dating back to Harry Truman swore on two Bibles—and Joe Biden used a family Bible dating back to the 1890s—there have been instances of Presidents opting to go other routes. According to his own account, sixth President John Quincy Adams said he swore on a book of law (though this has been disputed by several historians). Still, the newly affirmed President seemingly took a page from Quincy Adam's book by asking to be sworn in by placing a hand on a copy of the Constitution itself.

To be clear, there is no requirement for the President to use a Bible or anything like it. Instead, the Constitution (**Article 2 § Section 1 § Clause 8**) simply states that the incoming President must:

> ... [T]AKE THE FOLLOWING OATH OR AFFIRMATION:—"I DO SOLEMNLY SWEAR (OR AFFIRM) THAT I WILL FAITHFULLY EXECUTE THE OFFICE OF PRESIDENT OF THE UNITED STATES, AND WILL TO THE BEST OF MY ABILITY, PRESERVE, PROTECT AND DEFEND THE CONSTITUTION OF THE UNITED STATES."

As can be seen, there is no requirement to use props or swear/affirm on anything at all. However, even here the new President had riled up controversy. Every President, save the 14th Franklin Pierce, used the word "swear" instead of "affirm". Taking a cue from a forerunner that also did not use a Bible, this President refused to "swear" and would only "affirm". When asked to explain this decision, the President noted:

SWEARING IS A LEVEL OF COMMITMENT I CANNOT POSSIBLY ATTAIN. SWEARING MEANS THAT I WILL DO IT NO MATTER WHAT, WHICH WOULD NOT BE TRUE. I "AFFIRM" TO DO MY BEST AND ANYTHING WITHIN MY POWER, BUT NOT AT UNLIMITED COST. "AFFIRM" IS MORE IN LINE WITH MY CAPABILITIES AS PRESIDENT.

The President's political opponents were quick to strike at these words, claiming they show how weak this President is and saying the President could not be counted on and would not uphold the Constitution. To these remarks, the President shrugged off the criticism and stated:

I BELIEVE MY OTHER ACTIONS AROUND THIS CEREMONY SHOW EXACTLY HOW MUCH I WANT TO STICK TO THE CONSTITUTION AND AMENDMENTS, UNLIKE MY OPPONENTS AND PREDECESSORS THAT REGULARLY IGNORED THEM—RIGHT FROM THE VERY BEGINNING.

This response appeared to be in reference to the last part of the President's swearing-in ceremony. While most Presidents in the past century have also added "so help me God" to the end of the affirmation—both with and without prompting—it is again not a requirement. Even when Theodore Roosevelt was inaugurated in 1901, he ended with "And thus I swear" and there was no noticeable concern in the newspaper articles from that era. Yet in this day and age, the act of removing a reference to God that is not required created yet more polemics. Religious groups took notice and claimed that the White House will force an atheistic lifestyle on them, and that the actions undertaken during the proceeding inauguration speech prove that the Commander-in-Chief is willing to push the boundaries of the office.

Whether the President would attempt such an action—or even desires to do so—remains up for debate. The leader of the free world did state that the administration has no interest in dictating how people exercise their religion or lack thereof. On the other hand, the President made clear that the administration is against mixing any religious symbols with government functions and would be spending time and resources to make sure that if any do currently exist that they will be promptly removed. Some have already taken that statement as an attack on religion in general.

Yet, all these actions in the first few minutes of becoming head-of-state were only the tip of the iceberg for what the President had in store for the American people. What came next has sent shockwaves around the world and has already irreparably challenged the security, stability, and standing of the United States both at home and abroad. Immediately after finishing the affirmation, the President stepped up to the microphone and told the assembled audience and the millions more watching around the country and the rest of the world:

 MY FELLOW AMERICANS... THE PARTY IS OVER. I AM CANCELLING ANY AND ALL OTHER EVENTS ASSOCIATED WITH THIS INAUGURATION AS THEY ARE A WASTE OF TIME

AND MONEY. THE RESOURCES WE HAVE—AS A GOVERNMENT OF THE PEOPLE, BY THE PEOPLE, AND FOR THE PEOPLE—ARE LIMITED; AND I REFUSE TO WASTE THEM ON FRIVOLITIES. IT IS TIME TO GET BACK TO WORK.

The crowd that had been raucous just moments before was stunned silent. After intently gazing out at the masses and letting the mumbles die down a bit, the President continued:

TIME IS THE MOST PRECIOUS RESOURCE WE HAVE. AND IT IS THE MOST FINITE RESOURCE I HAVE AS PRESIDENT. I HAVE JUST FOUR SHORT YEARS TO ACCOMPLISH EVERYTHING I HAVE SET OUT TO DO. UNLESS, OF COURSE CONGRESS, IN ITS INFINITE WISDOM, DECIDES TO MAKE IT SHORTER.

A nervous laughter reverberated through the throng. While three Presidents have been impeached—with the most recent one being impeached twice—none have been convicted and removed from office by the Senate. Not being from either of the two major Political Parties, the independent President has no friends in Congress and could conceivably be removed should it come to that. And what the President did next may yet give rise to the first President ever being forcibly detached from their duly elected seat in the Oval Office.

Once the laughter quieted down, the President surprised

everyone by presenting and signing ten Executive Orders, each one more astounding than the last. While the early ones garnered large cheers from much of the crowd, as they kept coming a palatable itch began to spread among those in attendance. Even those who may have desired all these intemperate actions most likely were flabbergasted at how rapidly it was all happening, with no time to breathe and process between each announcement.

Our team of expert political analysts will break down and evaluate each of these ten Executive Orders in a series of upcoming articles, so check back often for updates, reactions, and fallouts from today's shocking revelations.

Meanwhile, social media has already erupted, both with proponents and detractors loudly declaring their benefits and dangers. That said, among all the noise, the world seemed to have coalesced around a specific nickname: **The Ten Pronouncements**.

At the conclusion of the speech, the President apologized to the dumbfounded crowd. That apology, though, was not for what had just transpired, but for what was to come next. Said the President:

 MY WORK FOR THE DAY IS NOT DONE AND I NEED TO TAKE A TRIP ACROSS THE COUNTRY RIGHT NOW BEFORE OTHERS REALIZE WHAT IS HAPPENING AND CAN COVER-UP WHAT THEY HAVE DONE. THAT MEANS I NEED TO BOARD AIR FORCE ONE AT THE COST OF MILLIONS AND MILLIONS OF DOLLARS TO

THE TAXPAYERS. WHILE I HAVE CAM-
PAIGNED ON AN AGENDA OF CUTTING
GOVERNMENT WASTE AND EXCESS, IN THIS
SITUATION I, UNFORTUNATELY, MUST ACT
IN OPPOSITION TO THAT PROMISE. FOR
THIS, I AM DEEPLY SORRY. THERE IS SO
LITTLE TIME, AND SO MUCH WORK TO DO.

Having apparently finished, the President gathered up all
the papers on the lectern and walked away. There was a
scattering of applause throughout the crowd, but in reality
there were mostly stunned faces both on and off stage,
standing with their mouths agape as the President headed
down the corridor and out of sight. With the President off
on this secret mission, all we can do now is wait for what
will undoubtedly be another astonishing day tomorrow.

GUANTANAMO BAY TO SHUT DOWN, TERRORISTS BROUGHT TO MAINLAND

PRESIDENT ATTEMPTS TO SIDESTEP HISTORY, CONGRESS, AND THE LAW BY COMPLETELY CLOSING GITMO AND RETURNING IT TO CUBA

The setting sun lights up the overgrown entrance to Camp X-Ray, the first detention center for enemy combatants at Naval Base Guantanamo Bay, on November 14, 2006. Photo and modified description by U.S. Army Staff Sgt. JON SOUCY, Public Domain, via Wikimedia Commons.

January 20th (Miami, FL) – Just minutes into the beginning of this administration, the new President issued the first of what would end up being ten Executive Orders. While it is traditional for the White House to provide the press with the text of such orders with detailed explanations and examinations beforehand, this President opted to surprise everyone and only produce that information after announcing them to the world. With the ink of the President's signature still wet on the official documents, many questions remained about not just the logistics of the President's actions, but on the legality.

In what can only be surmised as the President's top priority given its status as being the first order of business, the text stated that all detainees being held at Guantanamo Bay in Cuba were to be transferred to Federal prisons within 45 days. Further, once on the mainland, the President demanded that the courts start judicial proceedings against each of the prisoners within 90 days. The order was light on details about what the charges would be, who would bring them, and how the entire operation would be paid for, but it must be imagined that the *Justice Department* and *Department of Defense* would be involved. The President stressed that the individuals would be treated the same as any other prisoner in the Federal system—including access to public defenders if they cannot afford an attorney of their own.

The order also specifically drew attention to the wardens of these penitentiaries by highlighting that they would be personally responsible for guaranteeing the safety of the prisoners, though no penalty was laid out should they fail to do so. However, this unprovoked attack on Federal employees while offering preferential treatment to alleged terrorists rankled many of the President's opponents. One former nominee for President was quoted as saying:

 ISN'T IT OBVIOUS WHAT A MISTAKE IT WAS TO ALLOW THIS KNOW-NOTHING IDIOT TO ASSUME THE MOST POWERFUL SEAT ON

EARTH? THAT IS WHY WE CHALLENGED THE RESULTS OF THIS ELECTION—RESULTS THAT ARE STILL IN QUESTION. HOW THIS IGNORAMUS WAS ALLOWED TO STEAL THE ELECTION, I'LL NEVER KNOW AND WILL KEEP FIGHTING. BUT WHILE THIS TRAVESTY IS ALLOWED TO CONTINUE, WHAT YOU ARE SEEING HERE WILL BE THE RESULT. INSTEAD OF PROTECTING AMERICAN CITIZENS AND LOOKING OUT FOR THE PEOPLE WHO WERE BORN HERE, THIS SO-CALLED PRESIDENT HAS THREATENED HARD-WORKING FEDERAL EMPLOYEES IN ORDER TO PROTECT TERRORISTS!

Earlier during the inauguration speech, the President apparently foresaw such criticisms. While explaining the need for this order, the President said that the Constitution applies to all people—whether from the United States or not—and that we should not try to find and use loopholes to avoid upholding our own laws.

According to institutions like the **Center for Constitutional Rights**, circumventing American law is allegedly what the Guantanamo Bay Detention Center is infamously known for. The United States was able to permanently lease a small piece of Cuba starting in 1903 as a remnant from the Spanish-American war. Although Cuba has long called to remove the Naval Base—of which the Detention Center is a part of—from their island and for the United State to return full control of the property to them, each subsequent U.S. administration has refused to do so. Further complicating the issue is that after the 9/11 terrorist attacks on the Twin Towers in New York City, the Pentagon outside Washington, D.C., and other targets, President George W. Bush and his administration decided to use a camp at the Naval Base to detain and interrogate "extraordinarily dangerous people." Although the Detention Center became more prominent and well known during the Bush presidency, in practice Guantanamo Bay had been used for such purposes dating back decades.

Over the course of the Bush administration, the Detention Center became notorious for accusations of abuse, torture, sexual assault, and the general secrecy around the prisoners' treatment. While President Bush lost several court cases to try to maintain complete clandestineness and provide no due process rights to those detained there, the Supreme Court always stopped short of saying that the inmates had any Constitutional rights or that Guantanamo Bay fell under full United States jurisdiction.

During subsequent presidencies, Barack Obama and Joe Biden also attempted to shut down the Detention Center and transfer the prisoners to the mainland. President Obama was rebuffed immediately by both a military judge at Guantanamo Bay and then by Congress itself. In 2009 and 2011, Congress overwhelming passed legislation that effectively removed all funding that could be used to transfer detainees. As such, despite such promises, neither of those Presidents were able to completely shut down the Detention Center, although they were successful in reducing the population.

While speaking with limited members of the press aboard Air Force One following the inauguration, the question was posed how the administration intended to get around these seemingly settled points of law. The President instead insisted that the matter was not settled at all and that Congress had overstepped their bounds. The President told those assembled aboard the aircraft:

 DECIDING HOW PRISONERS ARE HANDLED IS COMPLETELY WITHIN THE PURVIEW OF THE EXECUTIVE BRANCH AND NOT SOMETHING CONGRESS HAS A SAY IN... THESE LAWS WERE UN-CONSTITUTIONAL WHEN WRITTEN AND REMAIN SO TODAY. SHOULD CONGRESS ATTEMPT TO ENFORCE THEM, MY ADMINISTRATION WILL GLADLY CHALLENGE THEM IN COURT.

A date in court seems inevitable no matter the circumstances, especially because this was not where the Executive Order ended. According to the text, once all detainees are removed from Guantanamo Bay, the entire Naval Base must be evacuated of all personnel and equipment within 180 days. Anything that cannot be taken with the troops is to be destroyed, leaving nothing behind. Finally, after all of that, the United States is to capitulate to Cuba's more than century-long demand and return the land to their sovereign control.

Many Cuban refugees and their descendants living in America responded negatively to this revelation. Reactions on social media ranged from disbelief to downright hostility. The general thread was that returning the land would be rewarding the Communist regime for their decades of horrific treatment against dissenters and supporters alike. Again, when presented with this, the President demurred and insisted:

As Commander-in-Chief, I have final say on all military operations. Since Guantanamo Bay is a Naval Base, and I say we no longer need it, then we do not and under my authority I can shut it down, forever.

Although former-Presidents Obama and Biden attempted to close the Detention Center and ease restrictions on the island nation, neither one considered closing the Naval Base itself, nor returning the land to Cuba. This step is far beyond what either imagined, and is contrary to an Executive Order by then-President Donald Trump in January 2018. Since Executive Orders are not law, Presidents can and have overridden the instructions of their predecessors. However, because this order does not explicitly repeal President Trump's order, the current President appears to be trying to avoid triggering a lawfully required administrative review. Such an action would delay the implementation of this plan by at least six months. When pressed on the issue, the President mostly sidestepped and did not provide a direct response.

Despite that, during conversations with reporters and when revealing the initial Executive Order, the President stressed a need to stand by what the courts may decide. The order has a specific clause which states that all parts of the Executive Branch will honor the findings, opinions, and requirements of the courts and stand by whatever they decide. While the Executive Order was particularly about the results of the trials for the detainees, the President stressed that the administration would always respect the will of the courts and would defer to their decisions, even if the Supreme Court ruled against them.

And that is not an insignificant risk, though the President did not seem concerned. Overall, it appeared that the leader of the free world was more focused on the symbolism of the order than on the substance and potential for its implementation. After all, the President ran on a platform of equality and the law being applied evenly to all people. It is an alleged naïveté that the President's opponents have pounced on in the past; that the idealism of American freedom must be tempered with pragmatism and the reality of facts on the ground—that freedom is never free and impossible without taking hard and often distasteful, but necessary, actions. Yet those people were not elected President, while the dreamer now sits in the Oval Office.

TÜRKIYE RECALLS AMBASSADOR IN RESPONSE TO ASSYRIAN GENOCIDE ACKNOWLEDGEMENT

PRESIDENT SURPRISES AND UPSETS KEY ALLY BY BRINGING LITTLE-KNOWN SAYFO TO THE FOREFRONT

The Hagia Sophia Grand Mosque (formerly The Church of Holy Wisdom) in Istanbul, Türkiye on March 1, 2013. In a sign of a growing autocratic approach, in 2020 Türkiye reverted the UNESCO World Heritage site's 85-year-old secular museum status and turned it back into a mosque, as it became during the 15th century Ottoman conquest. Photo by ARILD VÅGEN, CC BY-SA 3.0, via Wikimedia Commons.

January 20th (Ankara, Türkiye) – Türkiye (formerly known as "Turkey") has immediately recalled its ambassador back home for consultations in response to the signing of the second of ten Executive Orders the newly installed President of the United States presented during the inauguration ceremony. Further, the NATO ally and host to two American military bases—one of which contains tactical nuclear weapons—summoned the United States Ambassador for a dressing down, reportedly by the President of Türkiye directly. While Türkiye and the United States are often at odds on the world stage, the alliance between the two countries has remained steadfast for decades and issues are usually quietly resolved behind the scenes.

For instance, Türkiye and the United States went through a similar situation when President Joe Biden acknowledged the Armenian Genocide in April 2021. According to historians, during the onset of World War I around a million ethnic Armenians were systematically slaughtered or forcibly relocated at the hands of the Ottoman Empire, the predecessor to the modern nation-state of Türkiye. Türkiye has always and continues to deny such an event occurred and that the deaths of the Armenians—which they claim were far fewer in number than reported—occurred through legitimate wartime actions. In order to maintain good relations with Türkiye, many countries did not officially acknowledge these historic facts, although unofficial memorial services were often held in those same locales.

Starting in the 2010s, several European nations grew tired of Türkiye creeping towards a more authoritative government and away from democratic ideals, and used the opportunity to officially condemn the heinous crimes of the Ottoman Empire. Türkiye reacted with fury and fervor in each of these instances, but never broke off relations. Even with the United States, Türkiye had ages to prepare. As far back as the year 2000, while on the campaign trail, future President George W. Bush said he would make the acknowledgement if elected. When he failed to do so, his successor Barack Obama made the same promise, but also ended up deciding not to take action. In 2019, Congress passed a resolution acknowledging the genocide in response to Türkiye's invasion of northern Syria. Since the legislation was non-binding and President Donald Trump had a much cozier relationship with Türkiye than his predecessors, it was not until Joe Biden became President that the promise of recognition was finally fulfilled.

And it was those years of preparation that most likely softened the blow. The freshly installed President's Executive Order to grant the same status to the far less known Assyrian Genocide at the hands of the Ottoman and Persian Empires came out of nowhere. In all appearances, debates, writings, commercials, and the like, the new President never hinted that this was on the agenda, choosing to keep it close to the vest in order to suddenly thrust the issue upon the unsuspecting world.

Much like the Armenian Genocide, the Assyrian one—known as the Sayfo—also took place during the onset of World War I. Around 300,000 Christian Assyrians may have been massacred, although reliable numbers are difficult to come by. The Assyrian community traditionally had an oral history and records within the Ottoman Empire and then Türkiye were suppressed. Starting in the 1990s, the Armenian community began to have limited success bringing their plight into the public sphere. Inspired by what they saw, the Assyrians then began to organize campaigns around their own forgotten history. In order to have the necessary impact on the international scale, it required an entirely different style of outreach.

Sure enough, this is what seemed to attract the President's attention. Speaking while signing the Executive Order, the President said:

WHEN WE FINALLY ACKNOWLEDGED THE ARMENIAN GENOCIDE, IT WAS A GOOD START. BEFORE THEN, I THOUGHT I WAS GOING TO HAVE TO BE PRESIDENT IN ORDER TO EVER SEE THAT HAPPEN IN MY LIFETIME. IT WAS ONE OF THE ISSUES THAT HAS PRO-PELLED ME THROUGH THE YEARS IN ORDER TO GET TO THE SEAT I AM IN TODAY. HOW-EVER, JUST HAVING A GOOD START IS NOT NEARLY ENOUGH. IN ORDER TO NOT REPEAT THE SAME MISTAKES OF THE PAST, WE MUST LOOK BACK AND ACKNOWLEDGE ALL OF THE ERRORS AND HORRORS OF OUR FOREFA-THERS. HERE, WE'LL START WITH SOMETHING LESSER KNOWN, BUT WE'LL ONLY CONTINUE ONWARDS. THERE ARE MANY, MANY TRAVESTIES THAT HAVE OC-CURRED IN HISTORY, AND OTHERS THAT ARE STILL ONGOING TODAY.

With that, the President began to describe the history of the Sayfo before stating:

 THE RECOGNITION OF THE SAYFO IS JUST THE START OF CORRECTING THE MISTAKES OF CENTURIES OF REALPOLITIK AND END-ING THE IDEA THAT WE MUST PUT OUR IDEALS ASIDE FOR THE GREATER GOOD. IT DISGUSTS ME THAT THE UNITED STATES, OF ALL PLACES, HAS BEEN WILLING TO TURN A

BLIND EYE TO SUFFERING. IF WE DO NOT STAND UP FOR WHAT WE PROCLAIM THAT WE BELIEVE IN, THEN WE STAND FOR ABSOLUTELY NOTHING.

Despite these moving words and rallying for complete candor, the President appeared to still be playing a political game. While the Ottoman Empire and modern-day Türkiye seemed to be a major focus of this order, the Persian Empire—which gave way to today's Iran—was also called out. By many accounts, Persia actually attempted to help the Assyrians, at least at the beginning of the conflict. It was the Ottoman's invasions into Persia that left more Assyrians dead, although they certainly had assistance from some locals. When pressed for details on the calling out of Persia, the President outlined how at the end of World War I Persia had changed its tune and refused to allow refugees to return to their homes. Because of these actions, another 7,000 died in poorly maintained camps. This, the President surmised, was tantamount to committing the same crimes.

Representatives from Iran have not provided a response and do not appear poised to do so.

Noticeably absent from the order was any mention of the Kurds. Kurdish forces indisputably joined Ottoman troops in attacking and murdering the Assyrians. Today, there is no independent Kurdistan and instead the unique ethnolinguistic people are split between Türkiye, Iran, Iraq, and Syria. Unlike thoughts on the Assyrians, though, the President's belief that Kurdistan should be resurrected by taking the land from those countries and returning it to the Kurdish people is no secret. By not mentioning the Kurds in any way, the President appears to be deflecting the issue away from them in order to continue to support a separate agenda item.

And to be fair, the President did go out of the way in the Executive Order to make sure neither Türkiye nor Iran would be held responsible for the actions of their former empires. The text specifically says that no modern nation should be held liable, and only those nations that no longer exist could be admonished. Beyond that, the order does not create any penalties for failure to acknowledge the Sayfo, and says in plain words that no one should be "punished, refused services, or ostracized" for not following the guidance of using the word "genocide" to describe the events. In other words, the order does nothing more than change how the United States describes the events in the limited official documentation about it.

Despite this, protests broke out in front of the main U.S. embassy in Türkiye's capital Ankara, as well as near the aforementioned military bases. All staff have been confined to either the main embassy or the military bases while consulate and other satellite offices have been temporarily shuttered. An embassy spokesperson could not provide a timeframe of when they expected operations to return to normal but did ask all United States citizens in Türkiye to remain extra cautious and to refrain from identifying themselves as Americans. At this time, there is no guidance for U.S. citizens to leave the country.

Further complicating the validity of this Executive Order is the fact that it uses an unapproved House Resolution as part of its guidance. When Congress passed the motion related to the Armenian Genocide in 2019, they also introduced one for the Assyrian Genocide. That bill, though, never received a final vote in the House of Representatives, therefore no primer has ever been created to even base that component of the Executive Order on.

The President seemed unperturbed by these lapses and focused on the larger picture. Much like with the order to evacuate Guantanamo Bay, the President looked more concerned with the message being sent to the world than the actual implementation of these ideas and the consequences being faced. As stated by the President:

> TO ANY NATION THAT MAY FEEL DISPARAGED BY MY REMARKS, LET IT BE KNOWN THAT THE UNITED STATES OF AMERICA HAS NOT ALWAYS BEEN PERFECT, EITHER. WE ENSLAVED AN ENTIRE RACE OF PEOPLE; WE REFUSED TO GIVE EQUAL RIGHTS TO WOMEN AND THEN ALL GENDER IDENTITIES; WE TOOK CITIZENS OF JAPANESE DESCENT AND LOCKED THEM IN INTERNMENT CAMPS; WE PARTOOK IN A GENOCIDE OF OUR OWN AGAINST THE NATIVE PEOPLES OF THESE LANDS; AND WE HAVE COMMITTED AND CONTINUE TO COMMIT MANY OTHER DEVASTATING ACTS.

After discussing several other similar situations, the President continued:

> THE DIFFERENCE IS WE HAVE THE COURAGE TO LOOK BACK AND SAY, "WE ARE NOT OUR FOREBEARERS. WE WILL LEARN FROM THEIR MISTAKES AND STRIVE TO BE BETTER

THAN THEM!" BUT WE CAN ONLY BE BETTER IF WE ADMIT WHAT THEY HAVE DONE AND SAY, "THAT IS NOT ME! I WILL RISE ABOVE!" AND THAT IS WHAT WE ARE ASKING OF YOU. ADMIT THAT THESE HORRORS HAVE HAPPENED, BUT ALSO ACCEPT THAT IT WAS NOT YOU, EITHER, AND THAT YOU CAN AND WILL DO BETTER IN THE FUTURE. WE ARE HERE FOR YOU, BECAUSE WE ARE FRIENDS, AND FRIENDS TELL EACH OTHER WHEN THEY ARE IN THE WRONG.

To further hammer the point home, the President bemoaned the lack of knowledge among Americans regarding even the most pernicious of events like the Holocaust. Citing surveys by the *Pew Research Center*, the President stated that less than half of Americans even know that six-million Jews were killed by the Nazis during the second World War. Over a third of the respondents could not even hazard a guess at any number.

And it is this historical amnesia that the President appears to fear the most. As noted by the leader of the free world:

WHEN [NAZI LEADER] ADOLF HITLER PRESENTED THE *FINAL SOLUTION* TO ELIMINATE JEWS FROM THE FACE OF THE EARTH, OTHERS AT THE TABLE ENQUIRED IF SUCH ACTIONS WOULD ONLY UNITE THE REST OF THE WORLD AGAINST THEM. IN RESPONSE, HITLER BROUGHT UP THE ARMENIAN GENOCIDE AS PROOF THAT THEY

WOULD NOT CARE. NO ONE DID ANYTHING THEN, AND HE WAS CERTAIN NO ONE WOULD TAKE ACTION THIS TIME. SADLY, HE WAS PROVEN RIGHT. AND DESPITE THE OVERWHELMING EVIDENCE THAT WAS FULLY LAID BARE AFTER THE WAR, PEOPLE TO THIS DAY STILL DENY IT EVER HAPPENED OR BELIEVE THAT IT HAS BEEN OVERBLOWN.

Finally, before moving on to the next bombshell, the President summed things up with:

HISTORY WILL REPEAT ITSELF IF WE DO NOT ACKNOWLEDGE, TEACH, AND INTERNALIZE WHAT HAS TRULY HAPPENED. I REMIND YOU THAT HITLER WAS DEMOCRATICALLY ELECTED—SO DO NOT TELL ME THAT ANOTHER GENOCIDE COULD NOT HAPPEN HERE OR ANYWHERE ELSE IN THIS WORLD. WE MUST REMAIN FOREVER VIGILANT.

NATIVE AMERICANS REACT TO NEW PRESIDENTIAL ORDER

PRESIDENT APOLOGIZES TO INDIGENOUS PEOPLE FOR FIRST TIME; LOOKS TO SET UP REPARATIONS, INFRASTRUCTURE, INTEGRATION, AND MORE

From a traditional hogan in Window Rock, AZ, Dr. Jill Biden listens to Medicine Man Robert Johnson along with Navajo Nation President Ben Shelly, First Lady Martha Shelly, Speaker of the Navajo Nation Council Johnny Naize, and Barbara Naize on May 16, 2013. Photo and description by **CHUCK KENNEDY**, *Public Domain, via Wikimedia Commons.*

January 20ᵗʰ (Tahlequah, OK) – It has taken the entire history of the United States of America, but at long last a President has unequivocally apologized out loud to the indigenous people of these lands. The explicit apology follows much earlier ones to native Hawai'ians for overthrowing their kingdom, Black people for slavery, Japanese Americans for unjustly imprisoning them in internment camps during World War II, and others. Despite a resolution passed by Congress and signed by then-President Barack Obama in December 2009, no public declaration had ever been made before. According to **ROBERT LONGLEY OF THOUGHTCO** (*Longley, Robert. "U.S. Apology to Native Americans." ThoughtCo, Dec. 15, 2020, thoughtco.com /the-us-apologized-to-native-americans-3974561.*):

 IF YOU JUST HAPPENED TO BE READING THE 67-PAGE DEFENSE APPROPRIATIONS ACT OF 2010 (H.R. 3326), TUCKED AWAY ON PAGE 45, IN BETWEEN SECTIONS DETAILING HOW MUCH OF YOUR MONEY THE U.S. MILITARY WOULD SPEND ON WHAT, YOU MIGHT NOTICE SECTION 8113: "APOLOGY TO NATIVE PEOPLES OF THE UNITED STATES."

At the time, Native Americans were not impressed. According to individuals interviewed by various media outlets when the act was signed into law, by never actually announcing the apology, it did not truly exist. SAID **ROBERT COULTER**, then-executive director of the Indian Law Resource Center and a member of the Citizen Potawatomi Nation:

 WHAT KIND OF AN APOLOGY IS IT WHEN THEY DON'T TELL THE PEOPLE THEY ARE APOLOGIZING TO? FOR AN APOLOGY TO HAVE ANY MEANING AT ALL, YOU DO HAVE TO TELL THE PEOPLE YOU'RE APOLOGIZING TO... I HAVE HAD MY DOUBTS ON WHETHER

THIS IS A TRUE OR MEANINGFUL APOLOGY, AND THIS SILENCE SEEMS TO SPEAK VERY LOUDLY ON THAT POINT.

Yet this same resolution is what the new President is basing the entirety of these and all future actions upon. In the third of ten Executive Orders signed while the inauguration ceremony was underway, the recently installed President took the opportunity to not only publicly apologize to Native Americans, but to set up a committee to decide the fate of a plethora of outstanding issues related to the tribes—everything from fully implementing existing treaties going back hundreds of years; installing modern infrastructure on all tribal lands; creating "a realistic method of reparations"; and finding a way to either incorporate all reservations into existing States and Territories, or break them out as their own States or Territories away from current ones.

However, since this Executive Order is based upon the original law, it also reiterates its limitations. Namely, it does not allow any lawsuit against the United States, nor does it present any settlement offer of its own. Instead, the President has designated a commission that "shall be formed with representatives of the Federal Government of the United States, representatives of individual State and Territory Governments, and representatives of the many Native Peoples". There is no description of the makeup of this commission, how many members it should have, when they will meet, or how it will be funded. Instead, it presents a set of ideas that the working group will come up with answers and recommendations for on its own. Even if all of these divergent parties come to some type of agreeable compromise, anything they present will be non-binding and will have to be passed by Congress. Given the general split between the major Political Parties in Congress and their combined enmity towards the independent President, chances appear slim for any satisfactory resolution.

Representatives from the largest tribal governments such as Navajo Nation, Cherokee Nation, and others also expressed dismay at the lack of tangible measures and timelines. Further, in a joint statement signed by dozens of tribes, it was pointed out that the original Congressional Act apologized "on behalf of the people of the United States" and not the government itself. Although the President verbalized the admission, it was still the wording that was passed by Congress, and therefore the government has not accepted any culpability.

Other groups besides Native Americans were also concerned with the text of the order. The governor of Oklahoma—whose State is considered to be 43% "Indian land" according to a 2020 Supreme Court decision—expressed dismay at the idea that the State may be split in two or more in order to accommodate the decisions of the committee (a 2022 Supreme Court decision later reversed some of the conclusions of the 2020 case, giving the State of Oklahoma "jurisdiction over crimes involving non-Native Americans in Native American territory", according to **BUSINESS INSIDER**). In Arizona, New Mexico, and Utah—where Navajo Nation crosses over State boundaries—the governors were more muted in their responses, but expressed a similar concern. Even within tribes there was some agita. Hopi Reservation is completely surrounded by Navajo Nation and is noncontiguous, leading tribal leaders to wonder if they would be forced to be part of their much larger neighbor who has 25 times their population.

African American and Black community groups also raised

concerns around reparations being discussed here while they have been fighting for generations for the same. For these groups, though, the President already had a prepared response. During the signing ceremony, the President blatantly stated:

> BESIDES WHAT WE ARE DOING HERE, MORE APOLOGIES AND REPARATIONS ARE NECESSARY. BUT WE'LL START WITH THE INDIGENOUS COMMUNITY BECAUSE WE MUST ADDRESS ISSUES AROUND THE HEALTH, SAFETY, AND FUTURE OF THE PEOPLE LIVING ON UNDERSERVED RESERVATIONS RIGHT NOW.

When asked later to expound on these thoughts, the President noted that even though Navajo Nation is the largest of all of the tribal governments, it is still considered a food desert that is completely dependent upon the federal government for alimentary foodstuffs. Citing figures from government surveys, the President highlighted that over a third of the residents there lacked access to running water. Since water is a basic need for sanitation, medical issues also run rampant among the residents.

True to this description, Navajo Nation has the ignoble distinction of being the first place **Doctors Without Borders** deployed to within the United States. The organization, which is known more for going into warzones and third-world countries to provide necessary medical care for people who would otherwise have no other options, arrived in northeastern Arizona in May 2020 to help the nation get the COVID-19 pandemic under control. The lack of resources and running water only made the situation worse for the residents and those hoping to assist them.

Other tribal governments and areas are in similar or worse straits. Aboard Air Force One, the President said that this is the opportunity to right hundreds of years of wrongs, but that the solution could not be dictated from above. The reason for the lack of details around the structure of the commission is because the President does not want to pre-suppose knowing the answers. And of course, the President's opponents were quick to point out that the President had once again admitted to not knowing anything while implementing impetuous policy.

FEARS MOUNT OVER UNILATERAL NUCLEAR DISARMAMENT

IS THE WORLD GETTING CLOSER TO NUCLEAR DISASTER BECAUSE OF THE PRESIDENT'S ACTIONS?

Mushroom cloud of the bomb known as "Gadget", the first successful nuclear weapons test, seconds after detonation. Photo and partial description by the UNITED STATES DEPARTMENT OF ENERGY, Public Domain, via Wikimedia Commons.

January 20th (Chicago, IL) – Perhaps for the first time since 2010 and reversing the nearly continuous downward spiral that began in 1995, the *Doomsday Clock* to nuclear disaster may be ticking backwards.

The *Doomsday Clock* is a metaphorical representation maintained by the **Bulletin of Atomic Scientists** that helps give a visual representation of how close humanity is to destroying itself—most notably from nuclear weapons.

For instance, this has ranged from 17 minutes set in 1991 to just 100 seconds by 2020. The clock is not real-time and therefore does not change immediately no matter the situation in the world; not even during the Cuban Missile Crisis in 1962 nor when Russia started threatening to use any means necessary during its invasion of neighboring Ukraine in 2022. These events are arguably the closest the world has ever come to all-out thermonuclear war.

As such, the actions of the new President announcing the fourth of ten Executive Orders during the inauguration ceremony will not instantly set the clock rolling in one direction or another. However, the *Bulletin* was already expected to make their annual update in the coming days, so these pronouncements will definitely cause a significant recalculation. By press time, the *Bulletin* had not responded to any requests for comment.

In signing this particular Executive Order, the President did not simply declare a desire to reduce the available inventory of nuclear weapons at the disposal of the United States, but actually dictated specific commands for America to unilaterally disarm over 95% of its capabilities within four years. This would leave the entirety of the United States with around the same number of nuclear weapons as France or the United Kingdom, and indisputably result in Russia becoming the numeric leader in the atomic weapons field, followed distantly by China's growing catalogue. Just knowing that these two countries would have far more armaments than the United States may then, counterintuitively, make the world closer to annihilation simply because the United States' stockpile would not provide as much deterrence as it once did—a theory known as "mutually assured destruction" or "MAD". The President's political opponents highlighted those concerns in interviews and posts on social media following these announcements, especially in conjunction with the next two Executive Orders related to the United Nations and the deployment of American soldiers abroad that have further eroded global order.

See our follow-up coverage on these two Executive Orders on our homepage as both are rapidly developing stories.

Today, the United States has an inventory of over 5,500 nuclear weapons, although about 30% of those are considered "retired" and are in storage. Within the remaining arsenal, about 40% are readily available but are not attached to any delivery mechanism, while the remainder are able to be launched at any time. This means the United States has well over 1,600 nuclear weapons within its borders, stationed in other countries, and aboard various transports like ships and submarines that could be used at the press of a button.

This appears to be the President's motivation in ordering a unilateral drawdown of these ordnances. While announcing this Executive Order during the Inauguration Ceremony, the President stated:

STUDIES HAVE SHOWN THAT A MEASLY ONE HUNDRED NUCLEAR WEAPONS WOULD BE MORE THAN ENOUGH TO DESTROY THE WORLD AS WE KNOW IT. UNCONTROLLABLE CLIMATE CHANGE, NUCLEAR WINTER, FALLOUT FOR CENTURIES—THESE ARE THE LEAST OF THE ISSUES THAT THE SURVIVORS OF HUMANITY, IF THERE ARE ANY, WOULD HAVE

TO DEAL WITH. ONE HUNDRED NUCLEAR EX-
PLOSIONS ARE ENOUGH TO CRACK THE
CRUST OF THE CONTINENTS AND ASSURE
THAT WE HAVE REALLY BROKEN THE WORLD.
IF SO FEW NUCLEAR WEAPONS CAN DO ALL
OF THAT, WHY DO WE HAVE THOUSANDS?
WHAT IS THE POINT? WHAT MORE COULD
POSSIBLY BE NEEDED? DROPPING ADDI-
TIONAL NUCLEAR BOMBS IS ONLY GOING TO
PROLONG THE EARTH AND HUMANITY FROM
EVER BOUNCING BACK.

The *International Campaign to Abolish Nuclear Weapons* (ICAN)—which, according to its website, is "a coalition of non-governmental organizations" intent to see nuclear weapons banned worldwide—was quick to put out a statement in support of these actions, but also lamented that it was not nearly enough. Despite the explanation that the use of more than 100 nuclear devices worldwide would be devasting, the President's Executive Order would actually bring America's arsenal closer to 300 within four years. ICAN has made it clear that any nuclear cache is unacceptable and believes that having a single weapon is a violation of international law. A spokesperson for the organization in a press release stated:

EVEN A SINGLE NUCLEAR BOMB CAN KILL
UNTOLD MILLIONS AND CAUSE DEVASTA-
TION FOR GENERATIONS TO COME. TO THE
NEWLY INSTALLED PRESIDENT, USING
YOUR OWN WORDS, I ASK: WHAT IS THE
POINT OF HAVING ANY?

Neither the President nor any member of the administration has responded to these statements directly. Instead, the White House pointed us back to the text of the original order where the intent to limit the number of nuclear weapons available to the United States at any given moment is specifically laid out. In order to accomplish this, there are two main actions that the *Department of Defense* (DOD) is to undertake. First, the DOD is to initiate a prioritization where they will list out all nuclear weapons and give them an order for decommissioning, from least important to most—including the ones that are intended to be maintained. This activity is supposed to wrap up within 90 days, at which the point the armaments will begin to be disassembled.

To further assist in this effort, the President has ordered that any nuclear weapon kept outside the United States must be returned to American soil within 180 days. It is unclear if this means weapons aboard ships and submarines in international waters, and the White House has not responded to requests for further clarification. It does appear, though, to cover nuclear missiles at American bases in foreign countries, including members of NATO. This would in particular affect places like Türkiye (formerly known as Turkey), where protests are ongoing due to an earlier pronouncement by the President condemning the Assyrian genocide.

Other NATO allies also host American nuclear weapons, notably Belgium, Germany, Italy, and the Netherlands. Although the Russian Federation claimed one of its chief reasons for the aforementioned invasion of Ukraine was concern over the further proliferation of nuclear arms to its borders or among NATO allies, that did not come to pass. This became a noteworthy focus when Finland—with its

1,340 km (830 mi) long border with Russia—ascended into full NATO membership following decades of neutrality in response to Russia's aggression. Importantly, Finland is not a signatory to the United Nation's **Treaty on the Prohibition of Nuclear Weapons** (TPNW) and has abstained from voting on resolutions in the U.N. General Assembly concerning it. Despite this, according to a 2019 study sponsored by ICAN, 84% of the Finnish population want to sign on to the treaty.

Similarly, most of the countries in NATO, the European Union, and Europe in general have continued a policy of not housing such destructive armaments. The ones that do, though, as well as the aforementioned United Kingdom and France that have their own, reacted with measured trepidation. Expressions of "regret" were common among those who responded, but there were no outright condemnations, save for Türkiye as it was lashing out for unrelated reasons. Still, sources have told us there were screaming matches between the front line security officials and their international counterparts, as well as frustration from those same civil servants due to being caught completely off guard without warning.

Hawkish members of Congress also expressed grave concern over potentially losing leverage and bargaining ability with America's enemies and competitors. When asked about this aboard Air Force One en route to a still unannounced destination, the President said:

HOW CAN WE TELL OTHER COUNTRIES LIKE IRAN AND NORTH KOREA NOT TO MAKE NUKES WHEN WE HAVE SO MANY HERE? UNILATERAL ACTION IS SIMPLY THE RIGHT

THING TO DO. WE WILL NO LONGER USE THE THREAT OF NUCLEAR WAR AS A BARGAINING CHIP WITH THE LIKES OF RUSSIA AND CHINA AND THEIR PROXIES AND SIMILARLY MINDED ALLIES.

When told this response, one such Congressperson who wished to remain anonymous turned visibly red and shouted at our reporter:

HOW STUPID CAN THIS PRESIDENT BE? THESE COUNTRIES WILL SMELL OUR WEAKNESS AND COME FOR US. THIS ISN'T STRENGTH, IT'S SUICIDE!

It should be highlighted that Congress has not approved any funding for this project, not even the prioritization component. When asked about this, a spokesperson for the White House noted that as Commander-in-Chief, the President has wide discretion over the use of military funds. Congress had previously appropriated over $1 trillion to various military activities, much of which are nebulously vague. Due to this, the President feels assured that already allocated funds can be reprogrammed in a variety of ways.

United States Set to Leave and Abolish United Nations

PRESIDENT UNLEASHES HARSH TIRADE ON FAILINGS OF THE TRANSNATIONAL ORGANIZATION BEFORE ORCHESTRATING ITS ULTIMATE DEMISE

Flags of various member countries line one of the entrances to the United Nations Office at Geneva in Switzerland on June 15, 2012. Photo by TOM PAGE, CC BY-SA 2.0, via Wikimedia Commons.

January 20th (New York City, NY) – The dream of President Franklin D. Roosevelt to have a multinational organization that would ensure "life, liberty, independence, and religious freedom, and to preserve the rights of man and justice" is now dead.

These words were part of the **Declaration by United Nations** signed by the United States of America, the United

Kingdom, the Soviet Union, and the Republic of China on January 1, 1942 during the **Arcadia Conference**. Over the course of World War II, it was endorsed by an additional 43 nations. While President Woodrow Wilson failed to bring the United States into the **League of Nations** in the aftermath of World War I—despite being one of the architects of it and winning the Nobel Peace Prize for doing so—Roosevelt's successor Harry Truman was able to get Congress over the final hurdle to join the true **United Nations** of which this declaration was a precursor.

But perhaps the United Nations was already dead when it came into existence on October 24, 1945. Truman did not completely share Roosevelt's opinions on international affairs, and after the latter's death added components to the United Nation's charter that would hamstring it for its entire existence. Further, Truman worked around the United Nations and formed his own multinational force with NATO in 1949 and then invaded Korea without U.N. consent in 1950. Known as the "Truman Doctrine", the then-President saw it as the United States' role in the world to support all "free people" everywhere, especially against the rise of Stalin/Mao-style communism. With the Soviet Union and China both having veto power in the U.N. Security Council, Truman saw no recourse but to find loopholes in order to avoid dealing with them.

That stance remained true in one form or another throughout the entirety of the Cold War and beyond. On the campaign trail, the recently installed President of the United States was expressly critical of the United Nations, especially in light of their complete failure to stop Russia from invading Ukraine in February 2022 and all that happened in the war's aftermath. Throughout the entire conflict, Russia and China used their permanent veto powers on the Security Council to completely eviscerate any effort to stop Russia's expansionist plans. Contrarily, it was not the United Nations that brought about the eventual peace, but the combined efforts of Ukraine itself with NATO and other similarly aligned allies. The United Nations was proven completely impotent in the modern world, and that is seemingly why the then-independent candidate had asserted:

 THE STRUCTURE OF THE UNITED NATIONS IS IRREPARABLE WHEN DESPOTS HAVE THAT MUCH POWER.

With statements like that, it is perhaps why—of all of the Executive Orders the new President announced during the Inauguration Ceremony—this fifth one may have been the least surprising of them all, despite its massive impact across the globe.

By the text of the order, the United States is to immediately undertake a number of draconian actions that are all designed to ensure that the United Nations will collapse in short order so that no future administration could possibly revive it. Sure enough, this is a valid concern. Under former President Donald Trump, funding to specific U.N. agencies was severely curtailed or cut completely. When he was succeeded by Joe Biden, President Biden not only restored the funding to prior levels, but—according to the **Council on Foreign Relations** in April 2022—looked to "begin paying off part of the $1 billion owed in peacekeeping-related arrears."

In order to accomplish this complete obliteration, the President has created a multi-pronged attack. Of the most benign of acts, the President has ordered the recall of the entirety of the **United States Mission to the United Nations** (USUN), save for the Ambassador—formally known as the "Permanent Representative"—and Deputy Ambassador. The 150-member staff manages all of the political interests of America within the U.N. and includes two observer representatives to the General Assembly that are also members of Congress. In the end, only the top two executive positions are to remain.

However, they are only staying behind for one purpose: to use the United States' veto power in the Security Council. Within the Executive Order, the President clearly stated that regardless of the subject matter before the Security Council, even if it is in the interests of the United States, the Ambassador (or Deputy Ambassador if the Ambassador is unavailable) are to veto it. The simple idea is to make it so that the U.N.'s primary decision-making body will be completely paralyzed and cannot accomplish anything, even fund itself.

Meanwhile, without the USUN and only two staff members, the United States will no longer be able to attend any other bodies within the United Nations. Even if the Ambassador and Deputy Ambassador desired to, the President has ordered them and any other personnel not to, including appearing before the General Council. That means the General Council will be able to pass resolutions without even any input from the United States. However, all of those resolutions are unenforceable, anyway, without further movement by the Security Council. With the veto requirement in place, it would guarantee that the General Council would be completely toothless and useless, even on measures like trying to strip the United States of its standing and powers.

To justify this thinking, during the inauguration ceremony the new President began introducing the order with:

THE UNITED NATIONS IS A JOKE, SUPPORTS TERRORISTS AND DESPOTS, AND— WORST OF ALL—MAKES NO SENSE FROM AN ORGANIZATIONAL PERSPECTIVE.

NO OFFENSE TO OUR GREAT ALLY FRANCE, BUT WHY SHOULD YOU HAVE PERMANENT VETO CAPABILITY? FRANCE HAS 0.8% OF THE WORLD'S POPULATION AND 0.4% OF THE LAND AREA. THE ONLY REASON YOU HAVE THIS SUPREMACY IS BECAUSE YOU WERE A RACIST COLONIAL POWER PRIOR TO WORLD WAR II. COMPARED TO INDIA, TO BRAZIL, TO NIGERIA, TO VIETNAM, TO INDONESIA, TO ALGERIA, TO JAPAN... WHAT ARE YOU?

All the countries the President listed have populations and/or geographic sizes multiple times larger than France. More so, most of them are former colonies of European empires, with Vietnam and Algeria being specifically occupied by France.

After lambasting the other permanent members of the Security Council—including the United States itself—and various countries that have been part of the two-year rotations for the 10 non-permanent seats, the President turned towards other operational aspects of the U.N.:

BUT IT IS NOT JUST THE STRUCTURE OF THE SECURITY COUNCIL AND ITS PERMANENT MEMBERS THAT ARE NONSENSE, BUT ALL OTHER BODIES WITHIN THE UNITED NATIONS. FROM THE GENERAL COUNCIL DOWNWARD, EACH COUNTRY—NO MATTER ITS SIZE AND POPULATION—HAS ONE VOTE. AS SUCH, TUVALU WITH JUST 11,192 PEOPLE ACROSS 26 SQUARE KILOMETERS [10 SQUARE MILES] THAT CONSISTS OF 3 REEF ISLANDS AND 6 TRUE ATOLLS, HAS JUST AS MUCH SAY AS CHINA, INDIA, AND THE UNITED STATES—THE 3 MOST POPULOUS AND 3 OF THE TOP 7 LARGEST COUNTRIES IN THE WORLD.

The relatively unknown Tuvalu became a clear focus for the President as the speech continued and veered into other seemingly unrelated topics, but ones the President obviously felt were connected:

AND LET US BE CLEAR THAT THE UNITED NATIONS IS FAILING TUVALU, AS WELL. BEING BARELY ABOVE SEA LEVEL, THE ENTIRE COUNTRY WILL BE UNINHABITABLE WITHIN THE NEXT CENTURY BECAUSE OF RISING SEA LEVELS CAUSED BY MAN-MADE GLOBAL CLIMATE CHANGE. MEANWHILE, TUVALU IS ONE OF THE RARE COUNTRIES IN THE WORLD THAT HAS FULLY ACKNOWLEDGED TAIWAN AS ITS OWN INDEPENDENT

COUNTRY—A BRAVERY WE HAVE NOT EVEN SHOWN. YET BECAUSE OF THIS, TUVALU HAS BEEN PUT IN CHINA'S CROSSHAIRS, WHICH USES ITS OUTSTRIPPED INFLUENCE AND POWER IN THE UNITED NATIONS TO MAKE SURE TUVALU WILL NEVER BE PROTECTED, SECURE, OR FREE.

Under the "One China Policy", the U.S. and most other countries do not recognize Taiwan as its own independent nation, even though it is unofficially treated as such in most ways. Taiwan broke off from mainland China in 1949 during a civil war when the government of the **Republic of China** (ROC) retreated to the island in the wake of the overwhelming force of the **Chinese Communist Party** (CCP). The CCP, in turn, would go on to form the modern **People's Republic of China** (PRC). Due to the political realities of dealing with the PRC, only a handful of countries have fully recognized Taiwan's claims to independence. As the PRC has grown in economic, military, and nuclear power, some have even rescinded their prior recognition.

The President described several other situations similar to Tuvalu, doubling back on a few occasions. Most poignantly, the President discussed the "absolute ridiculousness" of an organization like the **United Nations Human Rights Council** (UNHRC) having as past and current members "such bastions of human rights" like Libya, Sudan, Afghanistan, Qatar, Rwanda, Saudi Arabia, Cuba, and many more countries with questionable—to say the least—human rights records of their own. With great agitation, the President told the crowd that the United States and its "natural allies" would not be dictated to by countries like these anymore.

Finally wrapping up this component, the President summed it up with:

 THESE ARE BUT A FEW SMALL CASES. THE BOTTOM LINE IS THIS: THE UNITED NATIONS IS COMPLETELY CORRUPT AND BEYOND REPAIR.

While the measures as laid out would certainly impact and perhaps paralyze the United Nations, they would not ensure its implosion. For that, the President decreed that all funding to the United Nations would cease immediately except for in a few key areas. The first was for the staff salaries of the personnel at USUN which would be paid directly by the United States. Further, certain peacekeeping missions would continue, but the U.S. would only pay the soldiers and staff it provided directly from the treasury and would not provide funding to the U.N. itself to distribute to others. Each mission would be personally approved and maintained by the President and could end at any time without warning as part of the President's broader plans to reduce American involvement around the globe, as seen in the Executive Order announced shortly after this one.

Citing statistics from the **Congressional Research Service** (CRS)—an agency of the Federal Government—the President noted that the United States is responsible for at least a fifth of the entirety of the United Nations' budget, both in required and voluntary payments, but not including what the country provides in manpower that is paid out of the regular Congressional budget. This varies greatly by program, from next to nothing for some to over 40% of the **World Food Program** (WFP). When asked later aboard Air Force One about cutting off funding to such a critical organization, the President emphasized that the United States is not against doing such acts, but just did not want to do them within the auspices of the United Nations. "The funds that have been set aside for something like the WFP," the President said, "could be reprogrammed for the same purpose, just with the United States leading the charge directly. We are not against this program; we are against the organization behind it."

The President also had earlier asserted not to be against internationalism in general, in spite of these decrees and the later ones. As stated by the Commander-in-Chief while signing this order:

TO BE CLEAR: THIS IS NOT AN ANTI-GLOBALIST AGENDA. THE "IDEA" OF THE UNITED NATIONS IS A FINE ONE, BUT THE INSTITUTION THAT SPRANG OUT OF THAT IDEA IS UNTENABLE. THE UNITED STATES WOULD BE INTERESTED IN JOINING A NEW TRANSNATIONAL ORGANIZATION THAT IS IN LINE WITH THE IDEALS THE UNITED NATIONS ESPOUSES, BUT WITH A STRUCTURE THAT CAN ACTUALLY FAIRLY SUPPORT IT. AND WE ARE GOING TO CONTINUE TO MAINTAIN ALL OF OUR OTHER EXISTING INTERNATIONAL AGREEMENTS, EVEN ONES NEGOTIATED BY MY PREDECESSOR THAT I HAVE BEEN A VOCAL OPPONENT OF. TO OUR PARTNERS IN NATO, I ESPECIALLY WANT YOU TO KNOW THE UNITED STATES IS NOT GOING ANYWHERE. WE ARE THERE FOR YOU AND YOU

FOR US, AND THAT WILL NOT CHANGE DUR-
ING MY ADMINISTRATION.

Despite claims of respecting NATO, the President immediately contradicted this statement with the next Executive
Order. Beyond that, the subsequent Executive Order after
that one further degraded trust in this President as a purveyor of more internationalism when what was presented
is largely being considered a new type of **Manifest Destiny**, instead.

*Check back on our homepage for updated details of
these rapidly developing stories.*

It also remains unclear if the United States will remain be-
holden to previously ratified U.N. treaties, such as the
**Convention against Torture and Other Cruel, Inhu-
man or Degrading Treatment or Punishment**. Further,
the United States is a signatory to many U.N. treaties like
the **Convention on the Elimination of All Forms of Discrimination against Women** that have not been ratified
by Congress. Legal scholars could not provide a clear answer on whether the United States could still maintain
and/or ratify treaties created by an organization that no
longer exists.

When questioned how the President intends to enact these
policies against the wishes of Congress, the White House
seemed unusually prepared. Compared to the prior Executive Orders, the administration had justifications at the
ready for overriding the power of the Legislative Branch to
control the purse and dictate the overall direction and expectations of the country and its executives.

First, in details provided to reporters and signed off by legal staff, the President intends to use the 1974 **Impound Control Act** (ICA) to immediately cut off funding for 45 days without the consent of Congress. While the ICA was ostensibly created to stop the President from reprogramming previously appropriated funds and hand control back to Congress, in practice it has done the opposite. Among the exceptions that allow the President to work around the will of Congress is a clause that says if another area of law requires that funding be stopped, the President must do so.

To this, the administration pointed directly to the 2001 **USA PATRIOT Act**, which contains a section that states providing material support for terrorism is a crime. In specific terms, material support consists of either "training", "expert advice or assistance", "service", and/or "personnel". With this definition, the President's representatives provided numerous examples of the United Nations providing all of these things to various terrorist organizations and state sponsors of terrorism—both directly and indirectly—and most notably with Hamas and Hezbollah.

In one egregious example, the White House pointed to a 2015 report authored by the United Nations itself that confirmed that Hamas and/or Islamic Jihad had stored and fired rockets from school buildings owned and operated by the U.N., a charge the body had denied for years until confronted with overwhelming evidence. Other points were not as concrete and dealt more with U.N. inaction in stopping countries like Russia and Iran from committing and/or sponsoring activities that could be classified as terroristic in nature.

If these arguments were not enough, the President also proposed that the Executive Branch has the right to terminate treaties at will. The **Treaty Clause** of the Constitution (**Article 2 § Section 2 § Clause 2**) only states that the President:

> [S]HALL HAVE POWER, BY AND WITH THE ADVICE AND CONSENT OF THE SENATE, TO MAKE TREATIES, PROVIDED TWO THIRDS OF THE SENATORS PRESENT CONCUR;

Being that this is in the Executive section, many have read this to mean the President has final say on the status of treaties, only needing Senate approval to enact them. There is no mention of repeal anywhere in the Constitution and the Supreme Court has never ruled one way or another. When presented with such cases, the Supreme Court in the past has ruled that it is a political question and therefore the Judicial Branch has no say in the matter. In practice, many Presidents have unilaterally withdrawn from treaties, such as when Donald Trump left the **Joint Comprehensive Plan of Action** (JCPOA)—more commonly known as the **Iran Nuclear Deal**—in 2018. However, in such cases, it is usually because there is some type of out clause that can be executed. President Trump said that Iran was not abiding by the terms of the treaty and therefore he could revoke it.

Similarly, this President has pointed to the same ability. Although the United Nation's Charter deliberately did not provide for a withdrawal, that idea is overwritten by *rebus sic stantibus*, or "things standing thus". In short, this doctrine of international politics maintains that a treaty—even one without an out clause—can become null and void when there are material breaches or circumstances change. The President has certainly made a case for this.

Beyond the story at home, in order to quickly cripple the U.N., the President has made it known that the administration will be reaching out to allies to recommend that they also withdraw from the U.N., especially those who feel they have been unfairly maligned by the organization. So even if somehow Congress and the Supreme Court get involved, the President will be able to argue that the point is moot and that the United Nations is gone forever, no matter which country is to hammer the final nail into the coffin.

ALLIES PROTEST RECALL OF AMERICAN TROOPS

NO MORE "WORLD POLICE" IF THE PRESIDENT'S NEW POLICY IS IMPLEMENTED

*U.S. Air Force Airmen supporting "Operation Allies Refuge" walk on the flightline at Ramstein Air Base, Germany on August 22, 2021. Photo and description by **U.S. AIR FORCE AIRMAN JARED LOVETT**, Public Domain, via Wikimedia Commons.*

January 20ᵗʰ (Ramstein Air Base, Germany) – The United States of America has not declared war on anyone since June 4, 1942 when Congress made such a statement against Axis partners Bulgaria, Hungary, and Romania during World War II.

To anyone born after that point, this may come as quite a surprise. After all, the United States has been involved in armed conflicts in Korea, Vietnam, Iraq, Afghanistan, and many other locales all over the world since then. Despite this, in every confrontation since the end of World War II,

the ability to do so has either come from a specific resolution passed by Congress or by the President acting in a
unilateral manner using funds allocated for general military
purposes. No official wars have been declared.

The Constitution clearly outlines that only Congress can declare war and maintain the necessary monies and forces to
do so (**Article 1 § Section 8 § Clauses 11 to 16**). Similarly, recorded discussions between the Founding Fathers
while writing the Constitution highlight that their wording
gives the President "the power to repel sudden attacks."
Coupling that conversation with interpretations of a component that calls for the Executive Branch to protect States
from invasion or domestic violence when Congress is unavailable (**Article 4 § Section 4**) seemingly has given the
President limited capabilities to respond in an emergency
situation. Yet, the definition of an "emergency" and the lack
of engagement by Congress to rein in the President has led
to a de facto shift in control.

While discussing Congress's abdication of its power and responsibility over armed conflict, Elizabeth Goitein of the
left-leaning **Brennan Center for Justice** stated in January
2020   (*https://www.brennancenter.org/our-work/re-
search-reports/congresss-role-military-conflict-growing-
gap-between-constitutional*):

THE 2001 AUMF AUTHORIZED THE USE OF
MILITARY FORCE AGAINST "THOSE NA-
TIONS, ORGANIZATIONS, OR PERSONS WHO
[THE PRESIDENT] DETERMINES PLANNED,
AUTHORIZED, COMMITTED, OR AIDED THE
TERRORIST ATTACKS THAT OCCURRED ON
SEPTEMBER 11, 2001, OR HARBORED

SUCH ORGANIZATIONS OR PERSONS." EIGHTEEN YEARS LATER, THIS LAW HAS BEEN INVOKED 37 TIMES TO SUPPORT CONFLICTS OCCURRING IN 14 DIFFERENT COUNTRIES, AGAINST ORGANIZATIONS THAT DID NOT EVEN EXIST ON 9/11.

As also laid out by Ms. Goitein, this clout has been used by successive administrations, Republican and Democratic alike. Prior to the existence of this specific legislation, Presidents used other means available to them or just plain ignored Congress in its entirety in order to deploy troops where they deemed necessary. There were occasions when the President at that time did not inform Congress and the Legislative Branch only found out through investigations. On other occasions, Congress explicitly forbade such actions, but the President refused to comply. In all of these circumstances, though—and again no matter the Political Party of the President—Congress refused to impeach and remove the President; thus, this behavior has been tacitly allowed and approved.

Apparently, since Congress has continually rebuffed taking back their Constitutionally mandated duty, the new President has decided to do it for them.

During the Inauguration Ceremony, the President ended the celebrations early and began to immediately sign a set of Executive Orders. The President had already made moves that were questionably within the purview of the Executive Branch's powers, most notably shutting down Guantanamo Bay, massively disarming the country's nuclear arsenal, and dismantling the United Nations. Each of these actions were seen by even the President's most zealous supporters as, at the very least, destabilizing. With this sixth Executive Order, the President has built upon that theme and angered allies all over the world, most notably in NATO. As the President told the still-reeling crowd:

FROM THIS POINT FORWARD, AMERICAN SOLDIERS WILL NOT BE DEPLOYED ANYWHERE IN THE WORLD WITHOUT A DIRECT DECLARATION OF WAR OR A SPECIFIC RESOLUTION BY CONGRESS. SINCE CONGRESS HAS NOT HAD THE COURAGE TO DO SO, I WILL PULL BACK POWERS FROM THE EXECUTIVE BRANCH THAT IT NEVER SHOULD HAVE HAD IN THE FIRST PLACE, AND RETURN OUR COUNTRY TO OUR CONSTITUTIONALLY MANDATED BALANCE.

While one part of the Executive Order did cover future situations in which the President pledged to make this a reality, the real issue lies in the fact that over 20% of the nearly 1.5 million U.S. troops are deployed elsewhere in the world. These numbers have ramped up over the years, especially in Europe after Russia's invasion of Ukraine in 2022 and around China and North Korea as the communist partners have increased pressure on American allies in their general vicinity. Specifically, the United States maintains around 750 military bases outside of the U.S. and its territories, not including boats, submarines, and comparable transports sitting in international waters.

Similar to plans for Guantanamo Bay, the President decreed that the United States should withdraw from everywhere outside its own territories unless—as noted before—Congress has passed or will pass legislation to keep a presence there. As such, the President ordered a review of every current mission, base, mass deployment (no matter whether for conflict or humanitarian reasons), and all other military-related matters to be completed within 180 days.

One of the key areas the President has turned to is the Constitution itself, which says that Congress has the ability to (**Article 1 § Section 8 § Clause 12**):

 [R]AISE AND SUPPORT ARMIES, BUT NO APPROPRIATION OF MONEY... SHALL BE FOR A LONGER TERM THAN TWO YEARS;

Within that review, the President has said that each mission must be tied to a specific resolution from Congress passed within the past two years. General resolutions will not count, nor will a specific resolution that is more than two years old. This part of the order has already led to great consternations and questions. For instance, although Japan hosts the largest number of American troops outside of home soil, decisions on deployment levels are determined largely by the Executive Branch and military divisions themselves. The **National Defense Authorization Act** as passed by Congress on a near-annual basis does outline specific funding for the maintenance and construction of bases located in Japan. Further, a section of the act calls for "enhancing cooperation with Japan, consistent with the Treaty of Mutual Cooperation and Security [b]etween the United States of America and Japan, including by developing advanced military capabilities, fostering interoperability across all domains, and improving sharing of information and intelligence..." Yet nowhere in the text is an appropriation for a named mission to Japan explicitly made, nor any timeframes declared. Due to this, the President's orders would seem to indicate that the personnel and equipment in Japan must be returned home. When asked about examples like this aboard Air Force One, the President told the press corps:

THE ANSWER IS SIMPLE. IF CONGRESS WANTS OUR TROOPS TO BE SOMEWHERE, THEY CAN DECLARE WAR OR PASS A RESOLUTION SPECIFIC FOR THAT DEPLOYMENT. I WILL NOT, UNTIL THE END OF THIS FISCAL YEAR, VETO ANYTHING THEY SEND ME AND WILL TAKE THEM AS ORDERS. IF CONGRESS DOES NOT DO THAT, THEN I HAVE NO CHOICE BUT TO BRING OUR SERVICEPEOPLE HOME.

How to move hundreds of thousands of troops home very suddenly is a largely open question. As part of the 180-day review, each commander is to create a withdrawal plan. Even if the commander finds reason to believe their mission is valid as the President has defined it, they are still to create a complete extraction stratagem that will ensure no U.S. personnel, equipment, or buildings and materials are left behind.

Unlike with Guantanamo Bay, though, there is no immediate call to implement each of these retreats. Instead, the President will be reviewing every report and overall proposal to determine which missions need to be wrapped up and when that is to happen. The only requirement is that once the withdrawal is thus ordered, it must be fully implemented within one year.

Because of this, from a practical perspective, no changes to deployment are happening at this time or even instantly at the end of 180 days. Based upon early feedback from the Joint Chiefs of Staff, the earliest they would expect even one mission to be concluded would be over two years from now, especially with already having to shut down Guantanamo Bay first, no matter the outcome of this order.

In spite of no immediate changes on the ground, that did not stop terrorist organizations and belligerent regimes from around the world from taking credit for "defeating the American devil" and "sending them running with their tails between their legs", according to translations of social media posts made by machine algorithms. Adherents from Daesh (Islamic State) even posted video of combatants firing weapons in the air in celebration. When shown some of these videos, one hawkish member of Congress just shook her head in complete disbelief and was completely lost for words.

Many experts anticipate that there will be a further clamp down on human rights in places like Afghanistan, Syria, Iran, and even Saudi Arabia—the latter of which has spent years attempting to modernize their image and economy. While Saudi Arabia is considered an ally of the United States and an important stabilizing partner among the more "moderate" Gulf countries, part of what has made them change is their desire to continue working closely with the United States. It is unclear if this potential downgrade in relations will encourage Riyadh to reverse course on hard-fought gains for women, minorities, and even rank-and-file citizens.

Beyond more volatile regions, other allies from around the world expressed great displeasure at this sudden loss of American support. NATO members in Europe, including Germany—which acts as the de facto home for NATO's military wing—reacted with disbelief. The Chancellor of Germany has already called the President directly to express the country's extreme concern about the impact of the loss of troops in Europe, most especially considering ongoing Russian aggression in the area. According to a readout from the White House, the President pointed to the inauguration speech where the newly installed leader stated:

 TO OUR **NATO** ALLIES, TO TAIWAN, TO JAPAN, AND TO EVERYONE ELSE WE HAVE MUTUAL PROTECTION PACTS WITH: I WANT YOU TO KNOW THAT NOTHING HAS CHANGED. EVEN IF WE END UP BRINGING ALL OF OUR TROOPS HOME, OUR ALLIANCES STILL STAND, AS DO OUR COMMITMENTS. IF YOU ARE ATTACKED, WE WILL RESPOND IN KIND, JUST AS WE HAVE AGREED TO. IT IS JUST THAT WE DO NOT NEED TO HAVE STAFF IN YOUR COUNTRIES OR REGIONS ALL THE TIME IN ORDER TO HONOR OUR OBLIGATIONS.

That did not assuage the fears of nations like Israel whose Prime Minister also called on the President to reconsider this decision. The leader of the sole majority-Jewish state in the world and the only true representative democracy in the Middle East is reported as saying:

WE LIVE IN A REGION SURROUNDED BY ENEMIES WHO DAILY CALL FOR OUR DESTRUCTION... ALTHOUGH WE HAVE MADE MANY NEW FRIENDS IN THE AREA OVER THE PAST SEVERAL YEARS, THAT FRIENDSHIP WAS NOT JUST BUILT UPON OUR OWN MUTUAL CONCERNS FOR PEACE AND SECURITY, NOR JUST ON OUR TRADE IN ENERGY, WATER TECH, AND FOOD, BUT THAT THE UNITED STATES WOULD SUPPORT ALL OF US AGAINST THE TYRANNY OF NATIONS LIKE IRAN. WITHOUT AN AMERICAN PRESENCE IN THE AREA, I FEAR OUR ENEMIES WILL ONLY GROW MORE EMBOLDENED.

When pushed to respond to accusations like these and other ones around the world, the President could not be stirred. Instead, the White House told reporters, allies, and adversaries alike that for now it is the status quo, that nothing has changed, and that Congress could easily keep it that way if they liked.

Concerns also extended to those people who have supported American troops in their host nations. After the disastrous departure of U.S. forces from Afghanistan in 2021, thousands of local workers were left behind and many ended up being tortured and killed by the Taliban in the vacuum created by the absence of American might. While under President Joe Biden there were attempts made to help extract people during the hasty evacuation and after the fact, the bottom line is that many people simply lost their lives while waiting for rescue. That black eye greatly diminished America's standing in the region and the world, and sent an unfortunate message to allies that perhaps the United States could not be counted on. Although some of that sting has worn off with time and later actions surrounding Ukraine, Taiwan, and elsewhere, many have never completely forgotten this lesson.

In an attempt to placate these fears, the President made it clear in the Executive Order that any plans to shutter American presence in a country must include steps to evacuate all people who worked for the United States and might be in danger. This pullout of human capital is required to take precedence well before any other part of the shutdown in order to ensure their safety. However, the President may face an uphill battle with Congress since the latter is still responsible for controlling immigration and refugees. With the acrimony already building between the Executive and Legislative Branches, it is highly likely that Congress will deny the President's request to accept tens of thousands of people, even just as a tool to stymie the President's ongoing campaigns.

AFTER BULLDOZING INTERNATIONALISM, PRESIDENT ANNOUNCES "NEW MANIFEST DESTINY"

WHICH NATIONS ARE MOST LIKELY TO JOIN AN EXPANDED UNITED STATES?

*The painting **AMERICAN PROGRESS (1872)** by **JOHN GAST**, Public Domain, via Wikimedia Commons. Description from the same: This painting shows "Manifest Destiny", the belief that the United States should expand from the Atlantic to the Pacific Ocean.*

January 20th (Cape Alava, WA) – *Manifest Destiny*.

These two words elicit a strong response in the American psyche. Depending upon the person, this may bring feelings of exceptionalism; that the United States had—perhaps through divine providence—a mission to spread democratic ideals from the Atlantic Ocean to the Pacific, and to keep European empires out of these lands. For those people already living in the path of the expansionists, it was seen as a racist landgrab that displaced and killed millions, paving the way for a uniquely American territorial empire that denied freedoms to most and is still in existence today.

The term "Manifest Destiny" became a part of the public zeitgeist in late 1845 in response to a newspaper piece by John O'Sullivan. While it is debatable whether Mr. O'Sullivan coined the term himself, his zeal for its general sentiment caught the attention of the Whig Party, who derided the very idea. In an ironic backlash, this actually gave the previously little-heard phrase an enormous boost of attention and helped solidify the belief into a national movement.

Throughout the 19th century, the creed was used to further push Native Americans off of dwindling parcels, to attack neighboring countries, and to try to drive European powers out of the western hemisphere. Eventually, when the United States finally did reach from coast-to-coast and the time of "Manifest Destiny" was seemingly at an end, the themes it brought gave rise to the policies of hard territorial and soft diplomatic control far beyond the shores of the North American continent. This continued all the way through 1947 when the United States added the Northern Mariana Islands and Guam as the last two territories. This, coupled with the independence of the Philippines the year before signaled the end of America's direct territorial gains, even though the people of those territories still have limited rights under the Constitution. While America stopped directly adding territories, it instead worked to expand its sphere of influence all around the globe through both diplomatic and military channels—with a particular emphasis on the Middle East and Southeast Asia, and especially anywhere bordering communist-nations like Russia and China.

The freshly installed President would address the issues with the territories and its people in a separate Executive Order given during the Inauguration Ceremony. However, before doing that, the President presented a new vision for "Manifest Destiny" in this seventh-of-ten surprise proclamations.

For context, in the previous two Executive Orders the President had assumingly backed away from internationalism by orchestrating the utter destruction of the United Nations and ordering American troops to leave foreign lands. But here is where the President turned the tables and made an ultimatum that even the United States' closest allies are calling an unabashed attempt at creating a new world order—only one firmly under the thumb of a United States that would be answerable to no other body. Said the President:

 NOW, BEFORE I SAID THAT IF A COUNTRY WANTS TO HAVE OUR TROOPS STATIONED THERE, THE REAL SIMPLE ANSWER WAS FOR CONGRESS TO PASS SPECIFIC LANGUAGE TO MAKE IT SO. BUT THAT IS NOT ENTIRELY TRUE. THERE IS ANOTHER WAY: BECOME A PART OF THE UNITED STATES!

The President then went on to explain that the American

military is already stationed in far-flung territories like the aforementioned latest additions, along with others like American Samoa. In a more salient point, the President highlighted that one of the largest military installations in the world—**Joint Base Pearl Harbor–Hickam**—is in the former territory turned State of Hawai'i. With this example, the President went on to press the case:

> IF YOU WANT THE PROTECTIONS, FREE-DOMS, AND OTHER BENEFITS OF THE UNITED STATES, THEN THE BEST THING YOU CAN DO IS BE PART OF THE UNITED STATES. TODAY I AM ANNOUNCING A NEW MANIFEST DESTINY. THIS ONE WILL NOT BE BUILT ON FORCED TERRITORIAL EXPAN-SION, NOT ON PURCHASING ILL-GOTTEN LANDS FROM OTHER COUNTRIES, NOT ON WAR, AND CERTAINLY NOT ON CONTROL-LING FAR-FLUNG PEOPLE FOR THE SOLE BENEFIT OF THOSE BACK ON THE MAINLAND.

During this overview, the President referred back to the prior Executive Orders, again noting that the United States would no longer be the "world police". Instead, an image was presented of the United States protecting its own and helping through spreading American resources, technology, power, and democratic ideals via expansion and merger. For more industrialized countries, this could be a direct path to statehood. For those in the developing world, this could be a plan to come in via treaty as a territory, and that treaty would also include a blueprint to modernize the formerly independent country, invest heavily in its infra-structure, and make sure they have all the opportunities of

the existing States. These treaties, the President suggested, would include specific timelines and milestones for
a territory to become a State. This way, they would not be
"stuck in the quagmire we have created with our current
territories, a situation I will soon address and correct."

**See our live coverage on our homepage to learn
about this breaking story.**

Here it should be noted that by the Constitution (**Article 4
§ Section 3 § Clause 1**), only Congress can admit new
States into the Union. On top of that, according to another
section (**Article 2 § Section 2 § Clause 2**), all treaties
must be agreed to by ⅔^{rds} of the Senate. Finally, Congress
controls appropriations and spending in general (**Article 1
§ Section 9 § Clause 7**). The President, though, appears
to be counting on this and has asked in the Executive Order
for members of Congress from both chambers and all Political Parties to be involved in negotiations, should the
opportunity arise.

Yet that opportunity appears to be the biggest question
mark of all. Of course, the President cannot order any
member of the Legislative Branch to do an action against
their will, but they will most likely want to be involved. The
real question remains: which other nations would possibly
want to peacefully surrender themselves to the United
States federal government?

Our nearest neighbors are already not a good fit. Canada
to the north in many ways defines itself by how it differs
from the United States. Also, within Canada there is a constant battle with secessionists who already do not want to
be part of the nation they are in, most notably those in the
French-speaking province of Quebec. Going further north

one finds Greenland, which is part of the Kingdom of Denmark. Former President Donald Trump attempted to buy Greenland from Denmark, ostensibly for the rare-earth elements located there. Not only was he rebuffed, but the local government in Greenland passed laws to make the mining techniques necessary to extract those elements illegal, thus even limiting America's ability to work with them as a partner. Since the new President specifically mentioned not buying land, Greenland is out as well.

To the south is Mexico, which despite long being integrated in economic relationships, has struggled with gaining parity on the freedom of movement between borders for its citizens. A large portion of the population in the United States looks at Mexicans and their descendants as interlopers and it is doubtful there would be enough agreement in Congress to allow such a potential influx. During the original Manifest Destiny, there was a movement to incorporate all of Mexico, not just Texas, California, and the rest of the Mexican Cession that included most of the modern southwestern United States. However, former Vice President and Senator John C. Calhoun (D-SC)—who was heavily involved in making sure Texas would be annexed and become a State— forcefully spoke on the Senate floor against adding the rest of Mexico, stating in part:

 WE HAVE NEVER DREAMT OF INCORPORATING INTO OUR UNION ANY BUT THE CAUCASIAN RACE—THE FREE WHITE RACE. TO INCORPORATE MEXICO, WOULD BE THE VERY FIRST INSTANCE OF THE KIND, OF INCORPORATING AN INDIAN RACE; FOR MORE THAN HALF OF THE MEXICANS ARE

INDIANS, AND THE OTHER IS COMPOSED
CHIEFLY OF MIXED TRIBES. I PROTEST
AGAINST SUCH A UNION AS THAT!

While most would not dare say such an overtly racist statement out loud in the Capitol Building today—in any case,
not in a place where they may be recorded—that does not
mean the same sentiment does not exist among similarly-
minded Congresspeople, or at least among enough of their
constituents that they depend upon to maintain their jobs
and power. As such, it is highly unlikely any country where
the majority of the citizenry are Hispanic, people of color,
or any other current minority in the United States will be
able to pass through the auspices of Congress, even should
they be interested. That would seemingly wipe out any opportunity for the entire continent of Africa and the island-
nations of the Caribbean, although given the history of
slavery in America, the vast majority of those nations
would most likely prefer to keep their distance anyway.

These same Congresspeople may also fear the state of the
economy in places like this and throughout much of Central
and South America—a situation perpetuated by a disadvan-
tageous colonial past—and how much it would cost to bring
them up to the standards of even the worst-off States in
America proper. Billions of dollars have been invested in
Puerto Rico to no avail, and Congress may fear a similar
situation.

Members of the Republican and Democratic Parties might
also have concerns about the overall impact on Congress
caused by adding these nations. Each future territory that
rises to the level of a State will add two legislators to the
Senate and will require reallocating the 435 seats in the

House of Representatives—or creating legislation to adjust the number of seats and still needing to make some type of adjustment. Either situation will set off another round of redistricting, potential political gerrymandering, and the inevitable lawsuits as a consequence of those attempts; all of which were seen following the release of the most recent Census results that kicked off a similar process. Depending upon the political lean of the incoming country and the fallout it causes, both Republicans and Democrats may dread the possibility of adding more of the "other kind" to their chambers.

In places requiring less investment, the question becomes what could they possibly gain from joining the United States? Eastern Atlantic nations are for the most part already in the European Union or aspire to be in it. The European Union may also be arguably stronger than the United States in totality, at least from an economic and standard-of-living perspective. Those nations that are currently not in the European Union and are not attempting to join seem to prefer to be on their own, including the United Kingdom which left the E.U. in 2020 in what was known as "Brexit". Nations similar to Europe like Australia and New Zealand also have systems in place that make them more independent. Other close allies in the Asian-Pacific region like Japan and India have little reason to join up, too, and have cultural differences that may make them, if not incompatible, perhaps uncomfortable being under American patronage.

The countries that are most impacted by the President's withdrawal of U.S. forces are across the Middle East. But each of these nations like Jordan, Baharian, and Kuwait are usually some form of semi-Constitutional monarchy; and monarchies of any kind are incompatible with the United

States Constitution. And this does not even take into consideration that all of these places have State-sponsored religions, a clear violation of the First Amendment. Even a democracy like Israel with on paper comparable equal rights, culture, and economy and that is already deeply entangled with American politics has a system where religion plays an outsized role. To maintain their Zionist national character, Israel would have no interest nor ability to join up.

All this really leaves, then, are small island nations that are already dependent upon foreign aid and protection, many of which are sinking into the ocean as sea levels rise due to global climate change. If anything, this would be more of a fast-track for a refugee program, a risk that would be a nearly impossible sell to Congress.

So, who then will be the first to join the United States in this new Manifest Destiny? The simple answer is this...

Most likely no one.

RACE TO THE 51ST STATE: PUERTO RICO VS. D.C. VS. EVERYWHERE ELSE

WITH THE PRESIDENT'S BACKING, WILL THE TERRITORIES OF THE UNITED STATES ASCEND TO STATEHOOD OR, PERHAPS, FINALLY BE FREE?

A colored postcard, circa 1905, titled PLANTING SUGAR CANE IN PUERTO RICO. Photomechanical print by A.C. BOSSELMAN & CO., NEW YORK (PUBLISHER), Public Domain, via Wikimedia Commons.

January 20th (San Juan, Puerto Rico) – Since the time of Christopher Columbus, the island-territory now known as Puerto Rico has never been independent and free. For hundreds of years, it remained a Spanish colony until the United States "liberated" it in 1898. After that, it endured as a territory of the United States federal government despite multiple attempts to change the status quo in any number of ways. Yet, perhaps it is different this time and

Puerto Rico really will finally become a State, or sail off as its own sovereign nation.

During the Inauguration Ceremony, the new President surprised the world by suddenly presenting ten new Executive Orders. The eighth of these concerned the territories of the United States and specifically how having them not be fully integrated into the country goes against the ideals of the nation. Said the President:

> THE WHOLE THESIS OF AMERICA IS THAT THE PEOPLE SHALL NOT BE GOVERNED WITHOUT REPRESENTATION. YET THIS IS EXACTLY WHAT HAPPENS WITH OUR TERRITORIES! MILLIONS OF INDIVIDUALS HAVE NO VOTING POWER IN CONGRESS AND, UNTIL MY ELECTION, HAVE HAD NO HAND IN SELECTING THE PRESIDENT, WHICH IN TURN MEANS THEY HAVE HAD NO SAY IN SELECTING FEDERAL JUDGES. AND THESE SAME JUDGES HAVE DETERMINED THAT ONLY "SOME" PARTS OF THE CONSTITUTION APPLY TO THEM. HOW CAN WE EVEN TALK ABOUT EXTENDING FREEDOM TO THE REST OF THE WORLD WHEN WE CANNOT EVEN DO IT AT HOME?

Within the United States, there are five territories that have permanent populations: Puerto Rico, Guam, the U.S. Virgin Islands, American Samoa, and the Northern Mariana Islands. On top of these is the District of Columbia, which is strictly speaking not a territory—it is considered a "federal district"—but is treated very much the same. Beyond all of that are another 11 uninhabited islands, though many are in the general vicinity of other American States or possessions. Altogether, there are, according to the Census Bureau, over 4.3 million people spread out among these locales, most notably in Puerto Rico with 3.3 million citizens alone.

While with the prior Executive Order the President had tried to entice the rest of the world into joining the United States as new members, with this one the President attempted to induce a final decision on the fate of all of the existing American possessions. By the text of the order, in two years during the November general elections, each of the territories must put a set of questions on the ballot. Those questions were laid out as:

(1) Should this land and its people remain a part of the United States?

(2) If this land and its people remain a part of the United States, should it ascend to Statehood?

(3) If this land and its people ascend to Statehood, should they become an independent State, join with other territories to become a State, or join an existing State?

Based upon this, a territory could decide in the first question whether they wanted to be an independent nation or remain a part of the United States. Then, if the majority voted to remain in the U.S., the second question would determine whether they would preserve their present circumstances as a territory or become a full State with all the rights, responsibilities, and taxes that includes. This is important in that even if a person voted against staying in the United States, their opinion would still count on what to do in case their will were overridden by the majority. Finally, the last question throws a bigger wrench into the works by asking about potential ways of becoming a State: either going it alone, joining with other territories, or being a part of another current State.

This is not the first time something like this has been attempted. In 2012, a similar approach was taken in Puerto Rico, albeit in two steps. Initially in August 54% of the people voted to change the current relationship with the United States. Then in November, over 61% voted for Statehood while the remainder either voted for full independence or a "free association" that equated to a mostly independent nation, but with access to American resources and giving the United States government unfettered admission for other activities, mostly military in nature. Despite the result, Congress failed to take any action and Puerto Rico remained a territory.

More recently, on the 2020 ballot a single question was asked whether Puerto Rico should become a State. This time the results were much more subdued, with only 52% voting in favor. However, Puerto Rico once again remained a territory because Congress refused to move on these resolutions. According to the Constitution (**Article 4 § Section 3 § Clauses 1 and 2**), only Congress has the ability to decide the rules for the territories, in addition to the power to admit new States into the Union. As such, Congress has the sole say on the future of these lands.

Which is why it was a surprise that the Executive Order contained language that attempts to compel Congress to undertake action. In it, the President said that Congress must vote on the desires of the people and, should they want it, grant them their Statehood or independence within one year after the election. It is unclear from what statute the President is claiming the authority to take this step and it is highly likely that Congress may just ignore the Executive Branch. Past experience shows that the Supreme Court will generally stay out of "political" decisions between the other branches and will let them sort it out on their own. Given the acrimony already shown by Congress towards the independent President, it seems even more likely they will just disregard the order in its entirety, no matter the outcome of the vote.

But should ascension to becoming a State be the desire of the people, that previously listed third question brings up a myriad of possibilities. Take for instance Guam and the Northern Mariana Islands. The island chains are very close in terms of a relatively empty Pacific Ocean and may decide that together—with a population of over 200,000—that they would be a more reasonable and formidable force. Similarly, the U.S. Virgin Islands are next to Puerto Rico and may desire to be part of their much larger neighbor. Or perhaps one or both would want to become a part of Florida? On the other end of the spectrum, American Samoa is almost completely isolated from other populated U.S. possessions and therefore they might be better off on their own.

Joining an existing State, though, may be more palatable to Congress as it would ensure no additional Senators would be added to Congress from these lands. Since each State gets two Senators no matter their geographic or population size, the idea of American Samoa with less than 50,000 people having as much power as Texas, California, New York, and Florida may be a bridge too far. But if it were part of, say, Hawai'i—despite being over 2,500 miles away—then its additional population would barely move the needle on the distribution of Representatives in the House chamber.

This, of course, leaves the matter of the District of Columbia. It is an open Constitutional question whether D.C. can even be a State, nonetheless a part of another State. The Constitution (**Article 1 § Section 8 § Clause 17**) gives Congress the sole ability to create and maintain a federal district to act as "the Seat of Government" and mostly discusses States giving up land to make it possible. Based upon this and other scholarly examinations, it is still unclear whether the roughly 700,000 people in Washington can ever gain equal footing without a Constitutional Amendment, just as the 23rd assigned the district Electors for the Electoral College that previously selected the President; that is, until the most recent set of Amendments retired the Electoral College and replaced it with our current citizen-direct system of mixed ranked choice and negative voting.

However, it is hard to deny that D.C. still has a population larger than even a couple of States, and Puerto Rico more than twenty-one of them. To continue to deny people their rights for going on a century-and-a-half is, as the President said, the antithesis of what American soldiers have fought and died for. In that respect, although the President may lack the power to enact the desired policies, perhaps the shame of a 21st century colonial empire will be enough to shock Congress out of their blasé attitudes towards millions of their fellow Americans.

FULL CITIZENSHIP EXTENDED TO AMERICAN "NATIONALS"

PRESIDENT FINDS A WAY TO BYPASS CONGRESS, THE SUPREME COURT, AND THE WRITTEN LAW

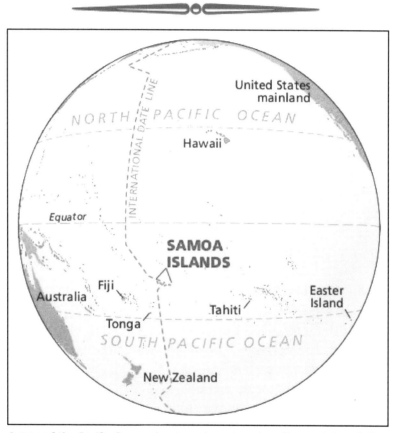

A map of the Pacific Ocean showing where American Samoa is in relation to other geographic landmarks. Image and partial description by **U.S. NATIONAL PARK SERVICE, RESTORATION/CLEANUP BY MATT HOLLY**, *Public Domain, via Wikimedia Commons.*

January 20th (Pago Pago, American Samoa) – "While the territories of the United States debate whether they wish to be a State or not," the President demurred, "I, unfortunately, cannot grant them the full Constitutional rights to which they are entitled due to the Supreme Court finding again and again that only some rights apply to the outlying possessions of the United States."

Thus began the ninth of ten Executive Orders the new President debuted during the Inauguration Ceremony. In the prior order, the President had demanded that each of the five populated territories and the District of Columbia make a choice about whether they wanted to remain in the United States or not, and if so whether they wished to be a State or part of another State—among other considerations. This, coupled with the seventh order that opened up the rest of the world to joining America as new territories and States, seemed to be about spreading the rights, privileges, and protections of the United States through expansion. However, here the President took time to highlight the failings of the system where the United States had already taken over.

As outlined by the President, due to the results of a set of trials in the early 1900s known as the "*Insular Cases*", the Supreme Court found that only "fundamental" rights were automatically extended to the territories. Other ones like voting, access to certain federal resources, and many more could only be conferred by Congress. Although some of this has been chipped away over time, generally the Supreme Court has upheld the overall conclusions of their predecessors, even when expressing that perhaps these policies are archaic. But instead of doing anything about the issue themselves, the courts have punted to Congress to correct the predicament they created.

And in that vein, Congress has slowly but surely seen to it.

Rights, programs, democracy, and other features of the mainland United States were extended to each of the possessions. Except, according to the President, for a specific one that the administration intended to address:

> EVERY PERSON BORN IN THE FEDERAL DISTRICT OR ANY OF THE POPULATED TERRITORIES IS A CITIZEN OF THE UNITED STATES. THAT IS, EVERYONE EXCLUDING THE FINE PEOPLE OF AMERICAN SAMOA.

Located deep in the South Pacific Ocean thousands of miles from the next nearest part of the United States, American Samoa consists of a handful of islands and atolls. During the early 1900s, the United States not only got Germany and Great Britain to give up claims on this particular set of lands, but also was able to procure agreement from the native inhabitants themselves. In May 2021, American Samoan Attorney Charles Ala'ilima testified before Congress saying in part:

> WHEN THE UNITED STATES FLAG WAS RAISED OVER PAGO PAGO HARBOR 120 YEARS AGO, OUR TRADITIONAL LEADERS BELIEVED THAT AS PART OF THE DEAL FOR TRANSFERRING SOVEREIGNTY TO THE UNITED STATES THEY WOULD BE RECOGNIZED AS U.S. CITIZENS. IT WAS NOT UNTIL 20 YEARS LATER THAT THEY WERE INFORMED BY THE U.S. NAVY THAT IN THE EYES OF THE FEDERAL GOVERNMENT THEY WERE NOT U.S. CITIZENS... THUS THE

STATUS OF "NON-CITIZEN NATIONAL" WAS INVENTED—A STATUS NO ONE IN THE UNITED STATES EVEN IMAGINED EXISTED UNTIL IT WAS IMPOSED BY THE FEDERAL GOVERNMENT ON NON-WHITE OVERSEAS POPULATIONS IN THE EARLY 1900S, AND A STATUS NO ONE IN AMERICAN SAMOA ASKED FOR.

Much the same was done in the other territories like Puerto Rico, the U.S. Virgin Islands, Guam, and even the Philippines before it was granted independence in 1946. Yet all other territories were eventually granted birthright citizenship by Congress, all apart from American Samoa. Instead, they remain "non-citizen nationals" and, in order to become citizens, have to move to one of the 50 States and then apply as if they were any other immigrant and not actually Americans.

In a quirk of the laws of naturalization, American Samoans can be fast-tracked as they only need to live in one State continuously for three months in order to apply for their full citizenship. The law (**8 U.S. Code § 1427**) says that a person must have resided within the United States continuously for five years as well as live in the State from which they are applying for three months. Since American Samoa is within the United States, people from there already have that requirement covered.

Nevertheless, they still have to jump through all the other hoops. This includes the English-language requirement, the politics and history tests, a check on "good moral character", and all of the fees and expenses associated with going through the process—something that can cost thousands of dollars, including attorney fees.

The Supreme Court had the chance to weigh in with the case known as **Fitisemanu v. United States**. John Fitisemanu was born in American Samoa but had lived in Utah for 20 years as a taxpayer, husband, and father of three. On several occasions, Mr. Fitisemanu attempted to gain employment with government agencies, but was thwarted from doing so because of his status as a "national". Finally, Mr. Fitisemanu attempted to vote in the November 2020 election and was again denied, thus prompting the lawsuit. In 2021 the *U.S. Court of Appeals for the 10*th *Circuit* found that the *Insular Cases* still applied and therefore denied his claim. That denial was left in place in 2022 when the Supreme Court—in an unsigned order—initially refused to hear the case. Eventually, though, the bench reversed course and agreed to settle the matter once-and-for-all.

Of course, this was not the first opportunity the Supreme Court had to revisit the *Insular Cases*, or at least the issue of citizenship. In 2015, the *U.S. Court of Appeals for the District of Columbia* heard **Tuaua v. United States** in which several American Samoans argued that under the **14**th **Amendment** they were guaranteed birthright citizenship for being born on United States soil. The judges instead unanimously found that not to be the case, especially because of the precedents set by the *Insular Cases*. When Leneuoti Tuaua, his contemporaries, and their legal team petitioned the Supreme Court in 2016, the bench also refused to hear it and thus tacitly agreed with the lower court's ruling.

It must be noted that at that time the Supreme Court was evenly divided between the conservative and liberal wings after the unexpected death of Justice Antonin Scalia. Since the Senate under the auspices of Majority Leader Mitch McConnell (R-KY) refused to consider then-President Barack Obama's nominee to the Supreme Court for nearly a year citing questionable reasonings, it meant that the court did not have a majority to even agree to hear that case, which in turn resulted in the judges being forced to leave the results as-is.

Since that time, the Supreme Court was transformed under former President Donald Trump and Mr. McConnell into one that was not only majority conservative with a 6-3 advantage, but that also moved ideologically far to the right even beyond the Republican mainstream. Thus, by the time **Fitisemanu v. United States** was heard and decided years later by the Supreme Court, the majority took the opportunity to not just confirm the *Insular Cases*, but to expand them and the powers of Congress in extreme and unexpected ways.

Prior to hearing this case, Justice Neil Gorsuch, writing in concurrence of the decision in **United States v. Vaello-Madero**—which ironically affirmed that Congress could exclude people living in Puerto Rico from programs like *Supplemental Security Income* (SSI), even if that same person worked and was receiving the benefits in a State prior to relocating to a territory—had written:

 A CENTURY AGO IN THE *INSULAR CASES*, THIS COURT HELD THAT THE FEDERAL GOVERNMENT COULD RULE PUERTO RICO AND OTHER TERRITORIES LARGELY WITHOUT REGARD TO THE CONSTITUTION. IT IS PAST TIME TO ACKNOWLEDGE THE GRAVITY OF THIS ERROR AND ADMIT WHAT WE KNOW TO

BE TRUE: THE *INSULAR CASES* HAVE NO FOUNDATION IN THE CONSTITUTION AND REST INSTEAD ON RACIAL STEREOTYPES. THEY DESERVE NO PLACE IN OUR LAW.

Despite these sentiments, Justice Gorsuch was unable to convince his contemporaries or bring them around to any of his views. Instead, he joined the liberal wing in dissent and the 5-4 majority of the remaining conservative justices decided several points. Namely, that:

- The **14th Amendment's** citizenship clause stating that "*[a]ll persons born or naturalized in the United States, and subject to the jurisdiction thereof, are citizens of the United States and of the State wherein they reside*" is literal to the word "State". Therefore, birthright citizenship is only guaranteed for those who are born in an actual State, not a territory.

- Under **Article 1 § Section 8 § Clause 4** of the Constitution, Congress can decide all laws and rules related to naturalization and citizenship. As such, Congress had the right to extend birthright citizenship to those born in places like Puerto Rico and Guam but deny them to American Samoa. At the same time, they affirmed Congress' sole authority to decide that birthright citizenship can be extended in other ways, such as to a child of an already-confirmed citizen when that birth takes place abroad.

- Further, under **Article 4 § Section 3 § Clause 2**, only Congress has the right to decide what, if anything, is to be done with the possessions of the United States that are not a part of a State. Because of this,

Congress can decide what applies to a possession and what does not, so long as it does not restrict or remove a right found to be "fundamental" by the courts. Once again, "fundamental" was still left vague and to be argued later.

- However, the courts did confirm that voting and being able to work for the government are not "fundamental", and therefore Mr. Fitisemanu is without any recourse but to seek full citizenship. Since that option is available to him, the courts did not see the process and expenses as a "significant impediment". They wrote in their decision that Mr. Fitisemanu could gain those rights through a well-defined methodology created by Congress and that he was at fault for not seeking that recourse over the 20 years he lived in Utah before filing suit.

Finally, in an unprecedented reinterpretation of the Constitution and internationally understood definition of the terminology, the justices found that naturalization and citizenship do not have to be one level; that there can be different types of citizens or citizen-like statuses with varying degrees of rights and responsibilities. In this case, the court affirmed that "non-citizen nationals" still belonged to the United States, but did not have all of the rights of full citizenship like voting, nor the responsibilities like jury duty or paying certain federal taxes. For further justification, the members of the court turned to examples of occupied areas during wartime like with post-World War II Japan from 1945 to 1952. Here, the judges argued that while Japan was arguably a possession of the United States during that time, there would have been no desire to have its people automatically gain citizenship. Therefore, Congress was able to define that relationship as a possession of the

United States and then again through treaty when it was released from that possession.

Another example was with rights that are allowed to be removed from certain individuals. For instance, the Supreme Court has upheld that convicts, even after serving their time, are not automatically entitled to regain their right to vote. Or similarly, people deemed mentally unstable are allowed to have their **2nd Amendment** right to bear arms restricted. By this logic, the majority argued, there already were several layers of citizenship as decided by Congress and State legislatures.

As a consequence of this ruling, many have feared that a literal second class of citizenship would be created, but Congress has been too deadlocked between Republicans and Democrats to pass any type of legislation that would bring about something remotely like that. Still, the potential exists, and attempts have been made to craft legislation what would align with the court's new philosophy, especially at the State level. Since these attempts have come from the more extreme wings of the Political Parties, leaders have thus far been able to tamp down such efforts.

Which returns us to the topic of the President's Executive Order. Here, the leader of the free world has demanded that all American Samoans and other outstanding "non-citizen nationals" be made full citizens. How then, given the Congressional powers as decided by the Supreme Court, could the President possibly make the nearly 50,000 people living in American Samoa and the perhaps 100,000 more similarly situated people currently living on the mainland in one of the States or the District of Columbia into this class?

One very explicit law (**8 U.S. Code § 1427, Clause F, Subclause 1**) says that the Executive Branch does—under a specific set of circumstances—have the ability to grant citizenship to extraordinary individuals. However, under **Subclause 3** of that same law, that is limited to just five people in total per fiscal year. As such, using this method would take at least 30,000 years to implement, even if every person could be found "extraordinary".

Instead, the President has decided to do an end-run around Congress by bending the existing laws as written. Within the text of the order, the President has directed the Attorney General and other relevant offices to take a seven-part approach for all "non-citizen nationals", starting with those currently residing in American Samoa:

(1) Set up a *United States Citizenship and Immigration Services* (USCIS) temporary field office and "service district" in American Samoa. With a "service district" covering the territory, the three-month residency requirement in another State will no longer be required.

(2) Fill in form "N-400 - Application for Naturalization" for each person and hand deliver it to them for confirmation and signature. If necessary, employees from the Attorney General's office should go house-to-house to gather the required signatures.

(3) Waive any need for biometric data, including fingerprints, since none are required by law.

(4) Modify the citizenship interview, English language test, history test, and "principle and forms of government" test. Instead, all of these requirements will be met with a one-question exam which will ask in

English, *"Is American Samoa a part of the United States?"* As the President wrote in the order:

> SHOULD THE PERSON UNDERSTAND AND ANSWER IN THE AFFIRMATIVE, THEN THEY SHALL HAVE PASSED THE TEST.

In support of this scheme, the President provided an interesting justification. While the law calls for all of these exams to be administered, it does not say how they are to be dispensed, nor how they should be graded. Because of this, the President argues, the Attorney General can modify them as the chief executive deems necessary.

(5) Accept the President's testimony that the person they are naturalizing is of "good moral character." It is unclear if the President intends to make this testimony for each person individually, or if the Executive Order counts as a blanket statement for all of them.

(6) Complete all of these steps during the hand delivery, approve the application, and administer the oath of allegiance on site.

(7) Eliminate any and all fees associated with the process that the government has control over.

With all of this, the President seems to be acting within regulations as required, but making a real-world impact. Once all the people of American Samoa are citizens, it cannot be taken away from them. More so, their children born afterwards will automatically inherit that citizenship from them, as covered in a different section of the law. Wrapping it up, the President told the assembled crowd:

I WISH I COULD EXTEND ALL THE RIGHTS AND RESPONSIBILITIES OF THE ENTIRE CONSTITUTION TO YOU. SADLY, EVEN BEFORE I TOOK OFFICE, I WAS STYMIED BY AN OUT-OF-CONTROL RADICAL SUPREME COURT THAT IS HELD ACCOUNTABLE TO NO ONE, AND A DO-NOTHING CONGRESS THAT WAS HAPPY TO LET YOU WALLOW FOR OVER A CENTURY. THIS IS BUT THE SMALLEST GESTURE I CAN DO FOR YOU. ALL I CAN PROMISE IS THAT WHILE I AM PRESIDENT, MY ADMINISTRATION WILL NOT TRY TO CIRCUMVENT OUR OWN LAWS ON MERE TECHNICALITIES.

PRESIDENT TO APPLY "NUTRITION FACTS LABELS" TO FOREIGN COUNTRIES

AMERICANS PUT IN DANGER BY RASH ACT TO GIVE EVERY NATION IN THE WORLD A "FREEDOM SCORE"

An example of a "Nutrition Facts Label" from a foreign country, namely Bangladesh. Photo on August 16, 2006 by **MAMUN2A**, **CC BY-SA 2.5**, *via Wikimedia Commons.*

January 20th (Washington, D.C.) – As an emotionally drained and exhausted crowd looked on, the freshly in-stalled President revealed the last of ten Executive Orders to kick off the new administration. People who had ex-pected to attend a party celebrating the first independent leader of the free world since George Washington were shocked to find the Inauguration Ceremony cut short and themselves made witness to the President's irreversible and world-shattering agenda, one that some are calling reckless and dangerous. But not even disarming America's nuclear capabilities, pulling troops out of strategic locations around the world, or letting terrorists run free were as thoughtless and perilous as what happened with this final Executive Order.

Here, the President announced something that is sure to upset almost every world leader, put American citizens and soldiers in the crosshairs, cost job-creating businesses billions of dollars, and will have the government making underhanded decisions for the average consumer. Said the President:

 WE ARE GOING TO APPLY SOMETHING AKIN TO A "NUTRITION FACTS LABEL" TO EVERY COUNTRY IN THE WORLD.

This unbelievable idea is based upon those little rectangles on the back of ketchup bottles that lets you know how many teaspoons you can "safely" squirt on your hotdog. In typical government overreach, the President intends to not only list out each nation on Earth and give it a rating on a yet-to-be-determined-and-defined scale, but then take that score and force companies to put them on their products. The President described this as a "Freedom Index" and said it will help consumers determine if the "area of origin" aligns to the government's definition of liberty.

At this time, the President is claiming that they will not use this so-called *Freedom Index* to bar any company from engaging in free and fair trade. Yet you can see the blood libel coming because the President said:

> THE UNITED STATES WILL NOT STOP YOU
> FROM DOING BUSINESS WITH DESPOTS—
> LIKE, SAY, SAUDI ARABIA—BUT THE FACT
> THAT YOU ARE SHOULD BE KNOWN TO THE
> WORLD AT LARGE.

Now, it should be noted that Saudi Arabia is one of our closest and most important allies in the Middle East, helping America keep terrorists at bay. More so, it is a country we depend upon to meet our energy needs. The United States government itself has plenty of commercial activity with Saudi Arabia. Will the government label its own programs poorly on the *Freedom Index*? Insulting Saudi Arabia in this way has already earned a strong rebuke from the Crowned Prince and caused gas prices to once again skyrocket over fears of retaliation.

So, as to the question of how this scale will be created, the President was, as usual, short on details and high on hyperbole. As "placeholder" names, the President chose four broad categories of where each and every country would sit. This starts with "Friends" that are, as the President described, "Representative democracies that try to give equal rights to all and pay living wages." As some examples, the President listed the United Kingdom, France, Brazil, Australia, Japan, and Israel.

The next layer down was "Frenemies", a slang portmanteau from the last millennia that combines the words "Friend" and "Enemy". Apparently, the President intends for our country to behave like it is a teenage girl in a clique. These outsiders we want to "hang with" but do not like consist of the aforementioned Saudi Arabia, Türkiye (formerly known as Turkey, a NATO ally that the President has gone out of the way to upset), China, and the Philippines. Basically, the President described these folks as ones that—although we do not have shared values—we will sometimes work with, and will in most situations try to avoid having a conflict with.

Coming up next were the "Neutrals", a much more nebulous category for those who really could not fit in anywhere else. By the President's definition, we do not like them, we do not want to be in bed with them, but we do not want to fight them either. A few potential "Neutrals" were Cuba, Libya, and Russia—the latter of which would have been a "Frenemy" prior to its invasion of Ukraine in 2022. Still, that act of aggression did not warrant the President considering Russia an "Enemy".

Naturally, "Enemy" was the last category. So, who are the United States' enemies? Well, these seem to be North Korea, Iran, and Venezuela. When pressed afterwards aboard Air Force One for other examples, the President's Communications Director explained that they were still working through the entire process, and that they will be releasing a complete list when it is ready. No one could give an exact timeline of when that might be.

The only thing the White House did say was that once the details are available, they will be focusing their resources on the countries in the "Friends" category because those are the ones that "are spreading ideals similar to our own." When asked again for a defined set of "American values", the President's deputy responded without actually answering anything:

I THINK YOU CAN SEE BASED ON THE EXEC-
UTIVE ORDERS THAT CAME OUT TODAY JUST
WHAT OUR IDEALS ARE.

Unfortunately, that is where the good vibes ended and the threats began. During the speech at the Inauguration Ceremony, the President laid out an ultimatum:

 IF YOU WANT TO PRESERVE OR EXPAND
YOUR RELATIONSHIP WITH THE UNITED
STATES, YOU WILL ONLY DO BUSINESS
WITH US, NOT OUR ENEMIES. YOUR
CHOICES ARE SIMPLE: EITHER YOU ARE
WITH US OR WITH OUR ENEMY; YOU CAN-
NOT BE BOTH. YOU MUST END RELATIONS
WITH OUR ENEMIES, OR YOU WILL ALSO BE
CONSIDERED OUR DE FACTO ENEMY, AND
WE WILL CUT YOU OFF IN EVERY POSSIBLE
WAY.

This ruffian talk was seen as a thinly veiled threat to Germany. German and U.S. relations were already showing signs of strain prior to 2022 due to the former's close relationship with Russia to meet their people's energy needs. Even after Russia invaded Ukraine, Germany stayed a major hinderance to completely cutting off Russian oil and natural gas supplies. After the war, Germany was quick to forgive Russia and even went so far as to certify and activate the **Nord Stream 2** pipeline from the motherland, enraging then-President Joe Biden. Strangely, prior to the Russian invasion, Biden had waived all sanctions related to the pipeline that had been put in place by his predecessor Donald Trump.

Still, Germany in the past has shown that it is willing to bend its policies and behavior, even with close economic partners. In the late 2010s and early 2020s, Germany was one of Iran's top trading partners, despite the latter having heaps of western sanctions against them. In 2019, Major-General Hossein Salami of the **Iranian Islamic Revolutionary Guard Corps** (IRGC), spoke at a widely publicized event in which he called for the destruction of Israel and even bragged about Iran's capabilities to do so. When asked specifically at the time by *The Jerusalem Post* whether Salami's words were antisemitic, the German government said they were merely "anti-Israel rhetoric" and brushed off all sincere concerns.

Yet, less than a year later, and under intense pressure from Israel and the United States, Germany relented and admitted the words and ideas espoused by Salami and the rest of Iran were actually antisemitic, causing a schism between the close partners. German Foreign Minister Heiko Maas then told *The Jerusalem Post*:

 SUCH STATEMENTS ARE ABSOLUTELY UNACCEPTABLE. WE STRONGLY CONDEMN CALLING FOR THE ANNIHILATION OF ISRAEL, LEGITIMIZING TERRORISM, AND SPREADING ANTISEMITIC CONTENT.

While this position reversal was easier for Germany since they were a continent away and had many other options to replace Iranian goods and services, that has not been the case for others in the area. Azerbaijan has a close relationship with Israel, one that is supported by the United States. But the country is next-door-neighbors with Iran and must not only live with them, but work with them in many ways in order to avoid war. While tensions have been steadily ratcheting up since 2016, Azerbaijan is careful not to push things too far. Although there have been tit-for-tat military drills on each other's borders and other recriminations in international forums and the media, the two do have a well-established level of cooperation that cannot be dismissed. It is unclear how a country like Azerbaijan can heed the President's unfair demands without endangering their own citizens and infrastructure.

These valid concerns did not seem to penetrate the inexperienced President's sensibilities. While the President said this ratings system and the requirements that went along with them were not designed to punish people—that the United States did not have a problem with the citizens of these nations, just their governments—it is impossible to see a situation in which the people would not suffer. Summing it all up, the President told the world:

WE DON'T CARE ABOUT WHATEVER IT IS YOU PROVIDE CHEAPLY TO THE UNITED STATES; WE'LL FIGURE SOMETHING OUT, EVEN IF IT IS MORE EXPENSIVE OR NOT AS GOOD. THE BOTTOM LINE IS THAT DOING THINGS THE RIGHT WAY IS BETTER THAN PLACATING DESPOTS.

Yet, ironically, the President seemed to disregard who may actually be the biggest despot of all.

A GREAT MANY PEOPLE WERE CERTAINLY STANDING BEFORE THE PLACARD, BUT IT DID NOT SEEM TO FIND MUCH APPROVAL. THERE WERE SO MANY PLACARDS; NOBODY BELIEVED IN THEM ANY LONGER.

FROM *AMERIKA* OR *THE MAN WHO DISAPPEARED* (INCOMPLETE) BY FRANTZ KAFKA

A NEW DAY DAWNS

PRESIDENT'S FIRST PRIORITY? ALIENS FROM OUTER SPACE

WHILE EXTRATERRESTRIALS WERE NOT FOUND, THE UNITED STATES GOVERNMENT WAS HIDING SOMETHING MUCH MORE NEFARIOUS

A crowd gathers on September 20, 2019 at the back gate of **AREA 51** *for the* **RAID AREA 51** *festivities. Photo and description by* **DAVID JAMES HENRY**, **CC BY-SA 4.0**, *via Wikimedia Commons.*

January 21st (Las Vegas, NV) – When last seen by the public, the brand-new President of the United States of America was boarding *Air Force One* to an unknown destination. In the hours beforehand, the President had disrupted the Inauguration Ceremony by ending the festivities and announcing ten new Executive Orders. While the world was still reeling from those massive shifts in internationalism, security, nuclear armaments, terrorism, and expansionism, the President set sights on the next most important thing...

Extraterrestrials.

Yes, the President of the United States went looking for aliens. And no, not the kind of aliens known for jumping across the United States' borders in the middle of the night, but actually those from outer space!

Our reporters were aboard *Air Force One* when it took off from **Joint Base Andrews** near Camp Springs, MD yesterday (January 20th) where the President and other members of the administration took questions and provided follow-up on the fallout from the President's **Ten Pronouncements**. However, after landing at **Joint Base Lewis-McChord** outside of Tacoma, WA nearly six hours later, the entire press corps was summarily taken from the plane and escorted off the premises to figure out their own accommodations or find their own way home.

At the time, it was uncertain why the President had chosen Washington State, but it became quite clear the next day. The President was apparently playing a game of subterfuge with another faction of the United States military, trying to obscure the true final destination without alerting those same people as to the President's intent. As the leader of the free world said during the conclusion of the Inauguration Ceremony:

> ... I NEED TO TAKE A TRIP ACROSS THE COUNTRY RIGHT NOW BEFORE OTHERS REALIZE WHAT IS HAPPENING AND CAN COVER-UP WHAT THEY HAVE DONE.

Now that secret place has been revealed, and it was the most mysterious of all; none other than **Area 51**.

Located over 80 miles from Las Vegas, NV in the middle of the desert, the exceedingly classified **United States Air Force** (USAF) facility known colloquially as *Area 51* is in reality *Homey Airport* and *Groom Lake*, as revealed by a 2005 **Freedom of Information Act** (FOIA) request that was finally fulfilled in 2013. Established by the USAF and the **Central Intelligence Agency** (CIA) in the 1950s, thanks to that FOIA request it is now known that the base housed many experimental aircraft and weaponry, including having captured enemy planes used for edification and practice during the *Cold War*.

Still, the extreme clandestineness around the base helped give rise to countless conspiracy theories. Most notably, many people believed that the government had been housing beings from outer space—either living or dead—and reverse engineered their technology, giving rise to many of our modern conveniences and military advancements. A whole cottage industry of "alien tourism" has also popped up in the nearby towns as travelers hoped to learn about the enigmas of what happened inside.

The chances of gaining any insight into the activities around *Area 51* were next to none before the President's visit today. Guards in the area surrounding the base are authorized and have used lethal force to keep the curious at bay. The closest anyone got outside of the aforementioned FOIA request was a 1994 lawsuit where civilian contractors in the area were found to have high levels of toxic compounds and metals in their body chemistry. They sued the USAF and the **Environmental Protection Agency** (EPA) seeking information from inside the base. At first, the federal government invoked "State secrets privilege" to quash the subpoena, but the judge on the case rejected this argument. In response, then-President Bill

Clinton used an Executive Order of his own, exempting "the Air Force's Operating Location Near Groom Lake" from EPA oversight. As such, there was no evidence and the case was dismissed, a ruling that was cemented when the **Supreme Court** refused to even hear an appeal of the case. Every year, each subsequent administration has renewed President Clinton's original declaration, thus maintaining the concealment.

While this President has not officially made any announcement, it is safe to say that it is highly unlikely the exception will be maintained given what happened in the early morning hours of January 21st.

After reporters were summarily dismissed, some stayed as close to **Joint Base Lewis-McChord** as possible to gather intel on what was occurring. At the time, a flurry of different military teams were seen coming onto the base and loading up gear onto *Air Force One*. It was later learned that much of this was actually video equipment so that the President could record every moment of what transpired inside *Area 51*. However, since the President has not released the unedited footage, the unfounded theories of what is happening in the shadowy base have not calmed down—despite the unexpected revelations the President did share.

According to an unnamed military member who joined the President on the two-and-a-half-hour journey to *Area 51*, every person was required to sign a specially crafted *non-disclosure agreement* (NDA). While discussing the existence of the NDA would not seem to violate its terms, apparently revealing anything the soldiers witnessed without express written consent from the President would be. Unlike corporate NDAs, the enforcement mechanism was not a monetary fine, but a jail term and admitting to treason for violating a direct order. The source said the President offered any soldier that was not comfortable with these terms the choice to leave the mission, no questions asked. There have been no confirmations at this time whether anyone departed.

According to **Federal Aviation Administration** (FAA) public records, *Air Force One* took off with its crew and paraphernalia at about 6:00 a.m. PT and landed at Homey Airport at about 8:30 a.m. PT. Upon landing, unconfirmed reports say the President was greeted by the base commander who then attempted to stop the country's leader and the rest of the crew from entering the facility, especially with recording accoutrements. The President is said to have challenged the head of the facility, asking if he was refusing a direct order from his Commander-in-Chief. When the base commander rebuffed the President, the President then called over **Military Police** (MP) that also went on the journey and had the base commander removed. It remains to be seen if the base commander will face charges, but rumors are that the President has insisted he face a military tribunal for his actions.

What fully happened inside is anyone's guess since, as noted earlier, the President has not released the unabridged footage. However, several hours after finishing the tour, the President held a live stream directly with the world, interposed with select scenes. The reason, the President said, for not providing the raw tape was because there were highly classified projects—both in transportation and weapons—that, for national security reasons, should remain as shrouded as they have been for decades. Yet, the President did want to emphasize something unexpected was still found inside, something that should never have been allowed:

 BEFORE GOING TOO FAR INTO ANY OF THIS, LET ME BE CLEAR THAT NOTHING OF AN EXTRATERRESTRIAL NATURE WAS FOUND INSIDE *AREA 51.* THERE WERE NO ALIEN LIFEFORMS—ALIVE OR DECEASED—AND ALL TECHNOLOGY WAS OF A STANDARD MILITARY OR CIVILIAN VARIETY. MUCH OF IT WAS ACTUALLY RATHER OUTDATED. YOU CAN REST ASSURED THAT MY TEAM AND I GAINED ACCESS TO EVERY PART OF THE FACILITY, ESPECIALLY THOSE THEY DID NOT WANT US TO GET INTO. SOMETIMES IT TOOK MORE... PERSUASION... THAN SHOULD HAVE BEEN NECESSARY, BUT WE WENT THROUGH EVERY NOOK AND CRANNY.

The President then went on to describe the previously unknown—at least officially—but highly suspected-to-exist underground testing facilities. Most seemed to be filled with the same benign type of research and the President lightly described some work on engine efficiencies, drone automation, and delivery systems that would be par for the course at any military research installation. It was then that the President turned deadly serious:

 WHAT WE DID FIND, THOUGH, IN SOME OF THESE ROOMS WAS PROOF OF PRIOR AND ONGOING DEVELOPMENT OF CHEMICAL AND BIOLOGICAL WEAPONS. UNDER THE "CONVENTION ON THE PROHIBITION OF

THE DEVELOPMENT, PRODUCTION AND STOCKPILING OF BACTERIOLOGICAL (BIOLOGICAL) AND TOXIN WEAPONS AND ON THEIR DESTRUCTION", WHICH WAS SIGNED AND FULLY RATIFIED BY THE UNITED STATES WAY BACK IN 1975, WHAT IS BEING DONE HERE IS COMPLETELY ILLEGAL, BESIDES BEING IMMORAL AND JUST PLAIN DISTURBING.

Ironically, this treaty was negotiated by the **United Nations**, an organization for which the President had just sowed the seeds of destruction the day before. The discovery of chemical and biological weapons in the United States was particularly upsetting to the current chief executive because then-President Richard Nixon ended these programs in 1969, well before any accords were crafted, signed, and ratified. President Nixon said at the time that the country would:

 ... RENOUNCE THE USE OF LETHAL BIOLOGICAL AGENTS AND WEAPONS, AND ALL OTHER METHODS OF BIOLOGICAL WARFARE. THE UNITED STATES WILL CONFINE ITS BIOLOGICAL RESEARCH TO DEFENSIVE MEASURES SUCH AS IMMUNIZATION AND SAFETY...

This unilateral action by President Nixon was echoed by a similar one declared by the new President in relation to nuclear weapons. During the Inauguration Ceremony yesterday, the President signed an Executive Order directing the United States to decrease its available nuclear armaments to only a fraction of current levels. Much like the present-day President, Nixon received a heap of criticism for removing an important tool of military deterrence and handing a potential advantage to America's enemies. In the end, though, Nixon's views won out. It remains to be seen if the same will happen this time.

Yet, because Nixon's views did become the norm, they also became the law. Said the current President:

UNDER CHAPTERS 10 AND 11B OF TITLE 10, BIOLOGICAL AND CHEMICAL WEAPONS, RESPECTIVELY, ARE ILLEGAL TO BE DEVELOPED, PRODUCED, STOCKPILED, TRANSFERRED, ACQUIRED, RETAINED, OR POSSESSED WITHIN THE UNITED STATES OR ANY OF ITS HOLDINGS. UNFORTUNATELY, THAT HAS CLEARLY OCCURRED. ANY PERSON WHO WAS INVOLVED IN THIS OR WERE AWARE OF WHAT WAS HAPPENING HERE—UP TO AND INCLUDING THE FORMER LIVING PRESIDENTS OF THE UNITED STATES—HAVE VIOLATED BOTH U.S. AND INTERNATIONAL LAW. AS SUCH, I AM MAKING SEVERAL CRIMINAL REFERRALS TO THE JUSTICE DEPARTMENT UPON MY RETURN TO D.C. TOMORROW.

While this has certainly created shockwaves at home, it has caused a much larger tsunami around the world. Condemnations were heard from signatories everywhere, including by nations like Russia and Syria that have been accused of violating the terms of the treaty in the past by allegedly deploying such weapons against adversaries, including civilians. Said one source within the Kremlin:

SEE, JUST AS WE ALWAYS ASSERTED, YOU WERE ALL DOING IT [DEVELOPING CHEMICAL AND BIOLOGICAL WEAPONS] ALL ALONG. OUR SUPERIOR INTELLIGENCE SERVICES KNEW THIS, AND WE UNDERSTOOD WE HAD TO RESPOND IN KIND; OTHERWISE, WE WOULD HAVE BEEN LEFT AT A TACTICAL DISADVANTAGE.

Given the immediate thrashing of the United States' reputation—one that the President caused by making these startling revelations in such a distressingly public manner without any consideration for the response from the rest of the world—did the Commander-in-Chief feel these revelations were worth it? When asked about how the nation should respond, the President proclaimed in an exasperated tone:

IF WE WANT TO BE "THE SHINING CITY ON A HILL" AND AN EXAMPLE TO ALL, WE HAVE TO MAKE CHANGES. ACTIONS LIKE THESE ARE EXACTLY HOW WE GOT INTO A NUCLEAR ARMS RACE THAT RESULTED IN ENOUGH WEAPONS TO DESTROY THE WORLD HUNDREDS OF TIMES OVER. SO, WE'LL NOW LIVE BY WHAT I SAID YESTERDAY AND CALL OURSELVES OUT FOR BEING WRONG.

OTHERWISE, HOW CAN WE EVEN BEGIN TO
REPAIR THE DAMAGE THAT HAS BEEN DONE?

However, there is another question that must be answered,
as well. That is: was the damage created by the President
going on this little alien hunt worse than the other potential
ways that this situation could have been addressed and
dealt with, options that the administration did not even
bother to explore?

On a "Quiet" Day, President Kicks Out Reporters and Toddlers, Invites in Sheep

White House Tries to Bring Order to Chaos with Chaotic Announcements About Order

Sheep tend to the grass in front of the White House in this 1919 photo courtesy of MISCELLANEOUS ITEMS IN HIGH DEMAND, PPOC, LIBRARY OF CONGRESS, Public Domain, via Wikimedia Commons.

January 22nd (Washington, D.C.) – Three days after taking the *Oath of Office*, the new President of the United States finally entered the Oval Office for the first time and then spent an entire day at work in the White House.

The prior two days had been quite exciting. On the first day—really half day, since the President was sworn in at noon—the Commander-in-Chief ended the Inauguration

Ceremony to announce a set of world-shattering Executive Orders that colloquially have become known as **The Ten Pronouncements**. Then, after boarding *Air Force One* and heading to the West Coast, the President and a military film crew dropped in on **Area 51** to reveal its secrets. No, it was not aliens; instead, it was an admission that the United States has secretly been developing chemical and biological weapons, a violation of U.S. and international law.

You can read more about all of these stories in detail. *Click here* to access our live blog with all the latest developments coming out of the White House.

After so many exhausting and exhilarating endeavors, it seemed like it was time for a quiet day. Yet even when trying to slow things down, the President has caused quite a stir.

▌ EMERGENCY ORDERS

According to unnamed sources, the President began the day by calling an all-hands meeting for everyone who is receiving a paycheck from the administration. Part of it was a meet-and-greet type situation, otherwise it was time for the President to set the tone for how work is expected to go from now on. The President noted that everyone in the room aside from the elected officials are just employees. As employees, the expectation is that they will work regular hours that are suitable for their position and personal needs, and that they were not required to always be at the administration's beck and call to respond to every little thing. One person in the room who had a recording device later shared some clips of the President's presentation—which did, we are told, include a PowerPoint. In the recording, the President stated to the captive audience:

NOT EVERYTHING IS AN EMERGENCY. YOU WANT TO KNOW WHAT IS AN EMERGENCY? HERE IS THAT LIST {ASSUMINGLY POINTING TO A SLIDE}. AS YOU CAN SEE, THIS IS SOMETHING LIKE THE COUNTRY IS BEING INVADED, A TERRORIST ATTACK, AN UNEXPECTED NATURAL DISASTER—MEANING NOT ONE WE KNOW ABOUT AHEAD OF TIME AND CAN MAKE PREPARATIONS FOR. BASICALLY, IT'S WHEN THERE IS A SUDDEN LOSS OF LIFE, OR THERE IS A POTENTIALLY IMMINENT DANGER TO THE UNITED STATES, ITS PEOPLE, OR ITS PROPERTY. WHEN THESE THINGS HAPPEN, IT IS ALL-HANDS-ON-DECK. OTHERWISE, I EXPECT YOU TO MAINTAIN A HEALTHY WORK/LIFE BALANCE, WITH A SPECIAL EMPHASIS ON THAT "LIFE" PART.

After this, the leader of the free world made it clear that no one, not even the President, will be instantly responding to "whatever dirt the media has come in with" or give in to demands for an immediate response by anyone, not even members of Congress. Here, the President called up other members of the transition team and division heads to explain that the administration was moving away from "constantly being in a reactive mode." Even though the President had already caused such massive waves, it was explained that none of what had happened could be categorized as a true "emergency". Each one, while major, was not a "catastrophe still in motion". Therefore, similar future announcements from the President could be addressed in an orderly, calm, and scheduled manner.

Further, in an effort to perhaps slow down the news cycle, the Communications Director let everyone know that daily briefings with the press would be eliminated. Instead, the President and relevant department heads would have a regular two-hour meeting slot set up, preferably on Friday afternoons. However, it would not be with the entire press corps, but instead with a single representative that would be chosen well in advanced to conduct the interview and disseminate information to the rest of the media. At this point, the President jumped in and said:

 AND TO BE CLEAR, THIS IS NOT GOING TO BE JUST CNN, FOX NEWS, POLITICO, THE WASHINGTON POST, AND ALL THE OLD GUARDS CYCLING THROUGH. I WANT TO MIX IN LIVESTREAM STARS, SOCIAL MEDIA PERSONALITIES, PODCASTERS, WHOEVER IS OUT THERE. AND IT DOES NOT MATTER WHAT IS GOING ON; WE ARE NOT GOING TO CHANGE THE SCHEDULE. IF THERE IS A STANDOFF WITH THE CHINESE NAVY IN THE SOUTH CHINA SEA AND I HAVE AN INTER-VIEW SCHEDULED WITH A FASHION BLOGGER, THAT APPOINTMENT IS GOING TO BE KEPT.

However, both the President and the Communications Director emphasized that the White House would always have its own film crews capturing the sessions and would post the raw video as well as put out press releases, video clips, and other such media that shows the administration's perspective. The Communications Director said that at the behest of the President:

> WE WILL NOT LET OUTSIDERS' FANCY EDITING TECHNIQUES DETERMINE OUR MESSAGING. WE WILL ALWAYS BE PREPARED TO PREEMPTIVELY DISPUTE POTENTIAL WAYS THESE INTERACTIONS CAN BE MANIPULATED FOR SPECIFIC AUDIENCES OR BE TAKEN OUT OF CONTEXT.

At this time, no one in the press has been officially notified of these initiatives, nor has any method been instituted to "sign-up" for these face-to-face meetings with the President, although Friday is fast approaching. When asked for comment, staff had apparently gone home for the day and could not be reached.

▌ OLD HOUSE, NEW TRICKS

As upsetting as these announcements may have been to the press, it must be noted that they have very little impact on the populous at large. For that group, the President had a few interesting tidbits to share.

First up, the President let the staff know about a number of steps that would be taken around transparency. At the top of the docket will be making the President's calendar completely unrestricted. More so, the President asked that a public facing website be created so that anyone could request to book themselves into an open slot on the calendar. The President highlighted that the Oval Office should not be available only for the political elite because they were all, in reality, subservient to the American people. As the President told the crowd:

> **IN CASE MY CHIEF OF STAFF OR MY EXECUTIVE ASSISTANTS ARE WORRIED, I WILL BE PERSONALLY MAINTAINING MY CALENDAR AND WILL BE BLOCKING OFF TIME FOR HEADS-DOWN WORK, TOO. AND PERHAPS A LITTLE BREAK, FROM TIME TO TIME?**

Yet, it does not appear that the President wants the public to always be at the White House. Specifically, the President made it known that all sorts of holidays and celebrations would be cancelled, including things like having a Christmas Tree. For this, the President not only noted objections based on "establishment of religion" grounds in a secular government setting, but expressed a general concern about the cost of such events for the American taxpayers. The price tag for each affair runs into the millions of dollars territory, especially considering the amount of security that is required. Overall, the President appeared to be trying to end what the administration considers "frivolities" while also adhering to a very strict interpretation of the first Amendment.

In that same vein, although the President emphasized that the staff should treat their professional life more like a "regular job", that did not mean it was still not a "place of work". Because of this, the President put forth the need for "a standard office environment" and less of the pomp and showboating of prior administrations. In other words, the President did not want more "photo ops" for political purposes, but instead wanted to spend the Executive Branch's energies and resources on doing the job of governing.

After this, a question was asked, perhaps flippantly, that, if not for "Easter Egg Rolls" for toddlers, then what would something like the White House Lawn be used for? To this, the President had an actual answer that proved that somewhere under that stern, enigmatic exterior was the capacity for fun, of a sort:

 BACK BETWEEN 1918 AND 1920, PRESIDENT WOODROW WILSON—IN AN EFFORT TO HELP WITH THE WAR EFFORT BY REDUCING COSTS AND CREATING USEFUL ITEMS—BROUGHT IN A FLOCK OF SHEEP TO HELP KEEP THE GRASS TRIM. WELL, I WANT TO DO THE SAME. LET'S BRING BACK SHEEP AND GOATS AND WHATEVER ELSE MAKES SENSE TO MAINTAIN THE LAWNS. LET'S HAVE MORE THAN A GARDEN; LET'S HAVE A FUNCTIONING FARM!

Later in the same soliloquy, the President continued:

 THESE ARE AMONG THE MORE ENVIRONMENTALLY FRIENDLY METHODS AVAILABLE TO US. AND IN THAT SAME VEIN, WHERE ARE OUR SOLAR FIELDS, OUR WINDMILLS, AND OUR GEOTHERMAL PUMPS IN SUCH VAST OPEN SPACES? WE NEED ALL OF THAT. THEN, AFTERWARDS, WE CAN SELL THE WOOL, MILK, HARVEST, AND ENERGY WE PRODUCE AND DONATE ANY EXCESS PROCEEDS TO A WORTHY CAUSE, OR PERHAPS

AN UNWORTHY ONE LIKE OUR NATIONAL
DEBT. WE CAN LEAD THE REST OF THE
COUNTRY—MAYHAP THE WORLD—BY THE
EXAMPLE WE SET IN OUR OWN ABODE.

Thus ended this so-called uneventful day at the White
House. At this point, we can only wonder: what new surprises will await us tomorrow?

NEW PRESIDENT "CAN'T UNDERSTAND" GOVERNMENT

PRESIDENT PROPOSES MASS CHANGES TO THE CABINET, PRECURSOR TO CONGRESSIONAL ACTION

A view towards the President's empty desk in the Oval Office. Photo by the WHITE HOUSE, Public Domain, via Wikimedia Commons.

February 5ᵗʰ (Washington, D.C.) – Who is in the President's Cabinet? Amazingly, it is a question that has never been answered because the "Cabinet" is not an organization that was created by the Constitution or any law. The only relevant clause of the Constitution (**Article 2 § Section 2 § Clause 1**) says that the President may require the opinion of the "*principal Officer in each of the executive Departments, upon any Subject relating to the Duties of their respective Offices....*" President George Washington interpreted this to mean he could create a working committee that regularly advised him, and it has been a tradition maintained by every subsequent President since then.

Aside from that, the Constitution says that Congress is the one that determines what the "*[E]xecutive Departments*" even are and who runs them (**Article 1 § Section 8 § Clause 18**). With that power, Congress has created 15 Executive Departments and has given them a place in the Presidential line of succession. These 15 people, along with the Vice President, are considered the core of the Cabinet, although throughout history others have been elevated to it and sometimes removed.

Just two weeks after shocking the world with a set of ten Executive Orders, the newly installed President of the United States has been relatively quiet while getting the White House in order. However, at this Friday's inaugural "Single Reporter Press Briefing", the President decided to let everyone in on the plans for the administration:

FRANKLY, I CAN'T UNDERSTAND THE FEDERAL GOVERNMENT. IT IS SO MASSIVE, SO UNWIELDY, AND MAKES NO SENSE STRUCTURALLY. BUT WHERE SHOULD WE EVEN BEGIN TO CORRECT THIS? IT SEEMS TOO DAUNTING A TASK, BUT I BELIEVE WE CAN MAKE SUGGESTIONS TO CONGRESS FOR MASS CHANGES IF WE START AT THE TOP AND WORK OUR WAY DOWN FROM THERE.

And starting from the top, the President then took to a white board to propose an entirely novel setup for the Cabinet, all while doing another end run around Congress so that existing law could be wrought to the Administration's purposes.

▎PRESIDENT DETAILS REASONING FOR SHUFFLING ENTIRE CABINET

During the interview, the President made it clear that while restricted from creating, merging, removing, and even re-naming federal agencies and departments, it was well within the President's purview to decide the makeup of the Cabinet and how information is filtered up to the Oval Office. This, the President argued, would allow the administration to create an internal structure where agency and department heads submit reports upwards to a select few that would represent key concerns through a wider lens instead of just special interests.

For instance, the President wants to merge the **Department of Commerce** and the **Department of Labor** into a single institution—and thus also merge the Secretary-level positions into a solitary job. Congress, though, requires both to exist. As such, the President has ordered the *Secretary of Labor* to report all findings and suggestions to the *Secretary of Commerce*, and then the latter would sit alone in the Cabinet and advise the President on the concerns of both departments. In the long run, the President intends to recommend an organizational structure that would align the Federal Government to this overall new Cabinet. However, as a type of "test run", the President will be making as many moves as possible without involving Congress.

Congress has not technically allowed any President to have reorganizational capability since 1984 when it granted those abilities to Ronald Reagan. In reality, Congress made it impossible for Reagan to transmit anything to Congress for consideration, so it was more a sleight of hand than anything else. Therefore, it is Jimmy Carter who holds the distinction of being the last President to get any type of executive reorganization through Congress, which happened in 1977. However, that was before the Supreme Court ruled that a "Legislative Veto" was un-Constitutional, and therefore the updated version of the law that was created after this ruling and attempted by Reagan has still not been fully tested. Presidents Bill Clinton, Barack Obama, and Donald Trump all attempted in one way or another to have Congress grant them the authority to do some type of reorganization of the government for a limited period of time, but none were successful.

Considering their defeats, this President is taking a different approach. Instead of trying to get near unlimited authority to make modifications—something a divided Congress would certainly be hostile to yielding to an unaligned President—the chief executive intends to create the desired setup through whatever actions are deemed plausible within the law. Once the top-level Cabinet is set up the way the President desires it, then those people in turn will look through all other federal agencies and departments and determine which ones belong under their tutelage. Said the President:

 EVERYONE'S FIRST GOAL IS TO ELIMINATE WASTE, INEFFICIENCY, REDUNDANCY, AND BUREAUCRACY. EACH OF MY CORE ADVISORS WILL BRING RECOMMENDATIONS TO ME ON HOW TO MERGE AND/OR ELIMINATE AGENCIES TO MAKE THESE REDUCTIONS.

EACH PERSON I HAVE HIGHLIGHTED IS AN
EXPERT IN THEIR AREA AND MUST PROVIDE
THAT INFORMATION SO THAT I CAN TAKE IT
TO THE MEMBERS OF CONGRESS, WHO
LARGELY JUST DON'T KNOW NOR UNDER-
STAND WHAT THESE EXECUTIVE AREAS DO.

When asked if there were concerns within the administration about its antagonistic stance towards Congress, the
President was defensive and said it was not meant to be
insulting, but simply a reality of not having a grasp on the
scope of the entirety of the federal establishment that they
were essentially responsible for. Said the President:

HOW COULD THEY? THEY CAN'T BE AU-
THORITIES IN EVERYTHING; THAT IS WHY
WE HIRE AND SURROUND OURSELVES WITH
PROFESSIONALS, SPECIALISTS, AND EX-
PERTS WHO CAN PROVIDE THAT INSIGHT.

That is not all the President has requested these advisors
to look in to. Hitting the President's ire in particular are
political appointees who do not belong in an organization.
As examples, the President listed appointing someone who
was against public education within the current **Department of Education** (DOE), having an oil-industry lobbyist
in charge of the **Environmental Protection Agency**
(EPA), or even having a vegan holding the reins of the
Food and Drug Administration (FDA). In each of these
situations, the President argued, the appointees have a direct conflict of interest with the overarching goal of these
agencies as defined by Congress. Still, the President did
not stop there, warning anyone who has prior connections

to industry groups that while their time working for the Federal Government may be up, their time in a federal penitentiary may be just beginning:

IF IT IS FOUND THAT THESE PEOPLE TOOK EVEN A STICK OF GUM FROM A LOBBYIST OR FROM SOMEONE IN THE GROUPS THEY WERE SUPPOSED TO HAVE BEEN REGULATING, I WILL MAKE SURE THEY ARE INVESTIGATED AND PUNISHED TO THE FULLEST EXTENT OF THE LAW.

Without the forthcoming detailed analysis to narrow down who this may impact, hundreds of people—including current agency and sub-agency heads—may be at risk. It seems that the President is quite intent on cleaning house of political appointees, especially those who were put in place to support either of the major Political Parties' perspectives and aspirations.

NEW CABINET CONSISTS OF A MIX OF EXISTING, MERGED, NEW, AND REMOVED POSITIONS

So, what would this new Cabinet look like? Well, instead of the 26 positions that make up the cabinet today—including the aforementioned 15 department heads, the Vice President, and the President—instead, it would be streamlined to just 14 individuals.

For some, the move would be more lateral, where an existing Secretary or agency head would fit into the role. These include:

- **The Attorney General** becoming **Freedom, Law, and Justice**;

- **Transportation** becoming **Interconnectivity**; and

- **State** becoming **Foreign Relations**.

It should also be noted here that the current Cabinet position of *Ambassador to the United Nations* was listed as being under **Foreign Relations**. Nevertheless, since the President had previously orchestrated the untimely demise of the U.N. through earlier executive action, it seems highly unlikely this position will have any importance, anyway.

Beyond that, even in these lateral moves, new responsibilities are expected. For instance, **Interconnectivity** will not just be about highways, trains, and planes, but will include communication methods like phones and the internet, subjects seemingly a part of the **Federal Communications Commission** (FCC). Meanwhile, other "new divisions" were fairly straightforward mergers of overlapping priorities:

- **Defense**, **Homeland Security**, **National Intelligence**, and **Veterans Affairs** becoming **Safety and Security** under the *Secretary of Defense*;

- **Treasury** and **The Council of Economic Advisors** becoming **Fiscal Management** under the *Secretary of the Treasury*;

- **Agriculture**, **Energy**, **The Environmental Protection Agency**, and **The Office of Science and Technology Policy** becoming **Science, Technology, and Environment** under the *Secretary of Agriculture*;

- **Commerce, Labor, The Trade Representative**, and **The Small Business Administration** becoming **Commerce and Labor** under the *Secretary of Commerce*; and

- **Health and Human Resources, Housing and Urban Development**, and **Education** becoming **People and Society** under the *Secretary of Health and Human Resources*.

Here it should be highlighted that certain functions are expected to be moved around. As an example, the **Census Bureau** would be transferred out of **Commerce** and put into **People and Society**. However, because Congress would have to make this realignment, the change would only be on paper for the time being. Then, there would be positions that would need to be split up:

- **Interior** becoming **Resource and Asset Management** and **Internal Relations**, with the former focused on the property-related elements and the latter on things like Native Americans and dealing with States. To account for this extra position, the current *Secretary of the Interior* would take on **Resource and Asset Management** while the ranked subordinate *Assistant Secretary for Indian Affairs* would be elevated to the Cabinet and be given the portfolio for **Internal Relations**. This latter selection would align with the President's prior Executive Order on fully integrating all Native American tribes into United States society, a key priority for the administration.

Finally, the President intends to create a few new positions, but fill them with similarly situated deputy appointees who have been confirmed by Congress for their current roles.

These include:

- *The Director of the Office of Management and Budget* will take control of **Government Operations**, which is charged with creating a "Shared Services Center" across the entire federal bureaucracy. This means any resources that can be used by multiple groups—like Human Resources, Information Technology, Finance, Material Acquisition, etcetera—should be taken from their individual departments and agencies and brought together under one roof. In order to get around the current Congress, the President has ordered each department and agency head to contribute to this new area from their existing allocations.

- *The Librarian of Congress* will be elevated to the Cabinet to act as the de facto head of **Arts and Culture**. While most of the listed duties already do fall under the *Librarian*, the President is asking for a much greater expansion of responsibilities, especially in areas that the United States currently has no agencies, such as with sports. As an example, among all nations, the United States is one of the few that does not support their Olympic athletes and makes them pay their own way. The President stated that this should change, so the *Librarian* will be the only one among the President's new advisors asking for a whole slew of new funding and agencies to buoy the many parts of art, sports, and culture that have no representation in the government right now.

Noticeably absent from these lists was the **White House Chief of Staff**. When asked about this, the President shrugged and succinctly said:

I BELIEVE THE VICE PRESIDENT AND I CAN REPRESENT ALL OF THE NEEDS OF THE EXECUTIVE BRANCH WITHOUT ADDITIONAL INPUT.

To accomplish this, the President laid out specific roles and responsibilities that would be expected for the two top members of the Executive Branch. For the **President** it would be "strategy and vision, risk management, communications and marketing, press relations, and inter-branch affairs and exchanges." With the **Vice President** the expectations were for "quality assurance, efficiency, accountability and ethics, safety checks and validations, and executive security."

EXECUTIVE LEADERSHIP AND CONGRESS RESPOND

Being that all of these newly named positions are not officially supported by Congress, the President cannot call the people who fill them "Secretaries". Instead, the President has created a new unpaid title called "Superintendent". With this, the current "Secretary of State" will also be called the "Superintendent of Foreign Relations"; the "Secretary of Agriculture" will also be "Superintendent of Science, Technology, and Environment"; and the "Librarian of Congress" will gain the title of "Superintendent of Arts and Culture".

While the non-department heads do not have much ground to complain because they are at the caprice of the President whether they serve in the Cabinet or not, the Secretaries of *Labor*, *Housing and Urban Development*, *Energy*, *Education*, *Veterans Affairs*, and *Homeland Security* can only look at this as a demotion through no fault of their own. This is especially troublesome to the Secretaries of *Labor* and *Housing and Urban Development* as they are listed above of the Secretary of *Transportation* in the Presidential line of succession, yet the latter will still be in the Cabinet while they have been relegated to watching from the sidelines. When asked about these issues, the President said:

 THIS IS NOT A COMMENTARY OR AN INDICT-MENT ABOUT THE JOB PERFORMANCE OF SPECIFIC DEPARTMENT OR AGENCY HEADS; THIS IS SPECIFICALLY ABOUT MAKING A COMPREHENSIBLE GOVERNMENT.

Later, the Commander-in-Chief continued this train of thought, saying in part:

 IN ORDER TO EVEN BEGIN TO UNDERSTAND WHAT WE SHOULD BE DOING, WE NEED A SETUP THAT REPRESENTS THE REAL CON-CERNS OF WHAT THIS COUNTRY IS ABOUT. NOW I WILL HAVE VOICES AT THE TABLE THAT MAKE MORE SENSE. NO OFFENSE TO THE *SECRETARY OF HOUSING AND URBAN DEVELOPMENT* AND THE *ADMINISTRATOR OF THE SMALL BUSINESS ADMINISTRA-TION*, BUT THEY ARE A SMALL PIECE OF THE PUZZLE TO ADDRESS THE GREATER QUES-TIONS OF "PEOPLE AND SOCIETY" AND "COMMERCE AND LABOR", RESPECTIVELY.

Neither of the leaders mentioned nor any other person

being pushed out or elevated to the Cabinet responded to a request for comment. Members of Congress have been equally quiet, but the *Speaker of the House* and the *Majority Leader of the Senate* put out a joint statement reminding the President that only Congress can change the makeup of the Executive Branch and the order of Presidential succession. When asked to respond, the Communications Director for the President said:

 WE AGREE, AND WILL BE SUBMITTING MULTIPLE PLANS TO CONGRESS DETAILING SCENARIOS TO REORGANIZE THE GOVERNMENT BASED ON THE RESULTS OF OUR INITIAL INQUIRIES.

WHAT WAS IN THE LATEST SET OF EXECUTIVE ORDERS?

THE PRESIDENT HAS SENT OUT A WIDE RANGE OF REQUESTS TO THE VARIOUS "SUPERVISORS" OF THE CABINET AND THEIR SUBORDINATES

*A Montessori classroom in Indiana on November 30, 2012. Photo and description by **KJJS**, **CC BY 2.0**, Public Domain, via Wikimedia Commons.*

February 9ᵗʰ (Washington, D.C.) – The President has delivered a new set of Executive Orders for numerous federal departments and agencies.

Why it matters: Since Inauguration Day, the President has attempted to use Executive Orders to completely remake the United States and the world at large, all the while sidestepping Congress. Over the past few weeks, these orders have taken an inward turn towards the organization of the White House itself and the Executive Branch in general.

Catching up: Just four days ago, the President redefined the Cabinet by creating a new unpaid position called "Superintendent" for 14 specific interests. Two of those positions were filled by the President and Vice President and the rest were assigned to existing department secretaries or elevated agency heads.

Of note: Under the President's reorganization of the Cabinet, several former members now report to their own equal-rank colleagues. For instance, the President has made several orders for the **Department of Education**, but that—as far as the President is concerned—is subservient to the **Supervisor of People and Society**, *a.k.a.* the **Secretary of Health and Human Resources**.

WHAT WAS ORDERED FOR EDUCATION?

Of particular importance, the President focused much of the orders on what to do with children...

- **New daily education plan:** The President wants a "new paradigm" in education where the focus is not on "subjects" but on "core competencies". Among these competencies are "critical thinking", "analysis", "empathy", "patriotism", "actualization experience", and "grit". Additional competencies are to be determined in working groups under the tutelage of the **Secretary of Education**.

- **School time expansion:** Along the same lines, the President wants to have the school day shifted to align with the clinically recommended hours for the various age groups, have school be in session year-round, have learning be more "self-paced", eliminate homework but have a longer school day, have food provided during extended meal periods, and other changes yet to be determined—again based on the working groups.

- **Yes, but:** Education in America is hyper local and it remains to be seen how a federal department with little authority and control could possibly compel these changes to come about.

THERE WERE MORE EDUCATION RELATED ORDERS?

Education was not limited to just primary and secondary, but extended beyond those early learning years...

- **Stop using the term "college":** Per the order, the government will be changing terminology from using expressions like "college" or "college-bound" to be more generic, like "further education". The President has also given a definition of this term to not just mean university, but also apprenticeships, internships, or other non-traditional education paths. "Universities and colleges have a monopoly in this country," the President said, "and we have a responsibility under the law to break up monopolies. Meanwhile, we are in desperate need of skilled tradespeople. We must support all paths to further education and stop pretending that pursuing college degrees is the only way to learn. More so, we need to end the gatekeeper role that private institutions have unfairly claimed."

- **Hiring full-time professors:** In the text of the order, the President expressed great disdain for how colleges and universities have gotten in the habit of hiring multiple part-time adjunct professors so they do not have to pay benefits or give them credits towards tenure. A core part of the President's platform was on decreasing underemployment or people needing multiple jobs to make ends meet. Further, the President accused the colleges and universities of illegal union busting by keeping their staff underpaid and with no way to organize. With this order, the President wants to see if access to loan programs for education can be tied to the percentage of staff that are full-time versus adjunct.

WHAT ELSE WAS ORDERED?

Aside from all these Executive Orders for the **Department of Education**, the President had a few other odds and ends requests. Of particular note were...

- **Independent contractors:** The newly rebranded **Supervisor of Freedom, Law, and Justice** née *Attorney General* has been tasked with going after organizations like the WWE for abusing the term "independent contractors" when paying their performers when they appear to fit the definition of an "employee". The same, the President said, is happening with the NCAA and other college sports organizations where the people are obviously not amateurs doing this on the side, but are revenue-generating employees.

- **Redefine unemployment:** In the same vein as employees, the **Supervisor of Commerce and Labor** is to change the measurement methodologies to get "real statistics for unemployment instead of the misleading hodgepodge we have now." Of particular concern was that unemployment only counts people actively looking for work and not those who have given up or do not report, and that it does not take into account "under-employment, people working multiple jobs, the poverty rate due to these low wages, and other similar measures and employer abuses." Based upon the text, the President does not want to see numbers gussied up, but instead wants to ensure they truly reflect the reality felt by people on the ground.

- **Keep your luggage: The Supervisor of Interconnectivity** was given a task closer to what would be expected of the position formerly known as the *Secretary of Transportation*. Here, the President has created a pet project to fundamentally change the boarding and security process within airports. Instead of checking bags before heading towards the terminals, all bags would be brought to the gate and checked there, no matter their size, and only small carry-ons would be allowed on the plane. This way, bags would not be transported on the tarmac between planes, but instead would be brought back into the airport to be moved between flights by their owners. The hope is that making people responsible for their own luggage would ensure it does not get lost and would cut down on issues that have only become more exacerbated over the years.

- **Profiling and air marshals:** In another airline related move, the President would like to see an armed air marshal assigned to every single flight instead of the less than 2% that have them now. Further, the order calls for training TSA agents in behavioral analysis so that they can talk with people in line and pull them out as needed for additional screening, using a profiling system more akin to what is seen in Israel.

- **Burying power lines:** In a cross-area order, as a matter of national security—thus involving the **Supervisor of Safety and Security** and the more than $1 trillion allocated to military efforts—the President has stated a need to harden the power grid to protect it against anything from EMP attacks to natural solar flares. Specifically, this includes building underground standing accessible tunnels that would house power lines and other infrastructure. At this time, only a study has been requested and no funds have been allocated to undertake the project.

WHAT HAPPENS NEXT?

The *Communications Director* for the President said that a lot more is planned and desired, but it will require buy-in and action from Congress. As such, the administration has requested something rare for a President during a first term: the ability to address both chambers of Congress in a **State of the Union** address.

Now, I want to speak very bluntly. I've got bad news, and I don't expect much, if any, applause. The American people want action, and it will take both the Congress and the President to give them what they want. Progress and solutions can be achieved, and they will be achieved.

From the *State of the Union Address* by President Gerald Ford on January 15, 1975

STATE OF THE UNION

PRESIDENT ATTACKS RATHER THAN ADDRESSES CONGRESS IN FIRST STATE OF THE UNION

IN A RARE FIRST-YEAR VISIT, PRESIDENT TRIES SHAMING CONGRESS INTO ACTION

Looking out at the Representatives, Senators, members of the Supreme Court, the Joint Chiefs of Staff, the President's cabinet, and other guests during the State of the Union. Photo by THE WHITE HOUSE FROM WASHINGTON, DC, Public Domain, via Wikimedia Commons.

February 26th (Washington, D.C.) – A few short weeks after making a request to do so, the President was able to appear before a joint-session of Congress to give a State of the Union address. However, this was a speech unlike any given since becoming formally known by that name in 1947—which coincidently was the first time the speech was broadcast on television. The last President to have a State of the Union during their first year in office was John F. Kennedy—although his successor Lyndon B. Johnson had one after Kennedy was assassinated and Gerald Ford also had one when Richard Nixon resigned. However, according to a **Congressional Research Service** report (*https://fas.org/sgp/crs/misc/R44770.pdf*) on the history of the State of the Union:

 SINCE 1981, PRESIDENTS HAVE AD-DRESSED A JOINT SESSION OF CONGRESS CLOSELY FOLLOWING THEIR INAUGURA-TION, BUT NOT AS AN OFFICIAL "STATE OF THE UNION" ADDRESS.

As such, Presidents like Reagan, Bush ("H.W." and "W."), Clinton, Obama, Trump, Biden, and others have chosen to give a more focused and stage-setting oration after they had only been in office for a few days. Of course, this President dramatically altered the world during the first hours of the administration. Because of these actions and the intentions of the White House, the President forcefully insisted that this be called a "State of the Union" and that all protocols be followed—including inviting members of the Supreme Court, the Joint Chiefs of Staff, the President's Cabinet, and additional guests.

The Speaker of the House must have been fascinated by the request and acquiesced, quickly putting together the session. Perhaps the Speaker and the other members of Congress thought this would be a chance to calm the rhetoric down and for Congress and the President to get on the same page? After all, in that last first-year speech by President Kennedy he told Congress, in part:

YOU ARE AMONG MY OLDEST FRIENDS IN WASHINGTON... I AM CONFIDENT THAT THAT FRIENDSHIP WILL CONTINUE. OUR CONSTITUTION WISELY ASSIGNS BOTH JOINT AND SEPARATE ROLES TO EACH BRANCH OF THE GOVERNMENT; AND A PRESIDENT AND A CONGRESS WHO HOLD EACH OTHER IN MUTUAL RESPECT WILL NEITHER PERMIT NOR ATTEMPT ANY TRESPASS.

If Congress was expecting a Kennedy-like hand outstretched in friendship—especially since the President did not provide a copy of the speech beforehand—they were in for a rude awakening.

SPEECH BEGINS WITH ACTS OF DEFIANCE

Not wasting a breath, the President launched into the State of the Union by asserting:

ARTICLE 6 § CLAUSE 3 OF OUR CONSTITUTION REQUIRES EVERY MEMBER OF CONGRESS IN THIS ROOM TO TAKE AN "OATH OF OFFICE", AN OATH THAT IS LAID OUT BY LAW THAT WAS CREATED BY YOUR PREDECESSORS AND DETAILED IN *U.S. CODE TITLE 5 § 3331.* IN THAT TEXT, YOU WROTE THAT YOU WILL "FAITHFULLY DISCHARGE THE DUTIES OF OFFICE" AND TO NOT DO SO IS A PUNISHABLE VIOLATION,

INCLUDING WITH FINES, REMOVAL FROM OFFICE, AND IMPRISONMENT. I'LL SPARE YOU THE NITTY GRITTY *OF TITLE 5 § 7311* AND *TITLE 18 § 1918*, BUT LET ME BRING YOUR ATTENTION TO A PARTICULARLY IMPORTANT CLAUSE.

At this point, the tension in the room was already palpable. Undeterred, the President quoted the aforementioned clause which states, in part, that it is illegal if anyone in Congress:

... PARTICIPATES IN A STRIKE, OR ASSERTS THE RIGHT TO STRIKE, AGAINST THE GOVERNMENT OF THE UNITED STATES...

The bewildered members of Congress gave each other baffled looks as if asking where this was all going, but otherwise remained silent. At this point, the President turned to the Justices of the Supreme Court that were in the front row and stared down at them with what can only be described as righteous fire. Never breaking eye contact with them, the President said:

WHEN SUPREME COURT JUSTICE ANTONIN SCALIA DIED IN 2016, PRESIDENT BARACK OBAMA DID HIS CONSTITUTIONAL DUTY BY PRESENTING MERRICK GARLAND AS A NOMINEE TO REPLACE HIM. THE SENATE'S JOB WAS SIMPLE: INTERVIEW AND VET THE CANDIDATE, THEN CAST A YAY OR NAY VOTE. THAT WAS ALL THERE SHOULD

HAVE BEEN TO IT! INSTEAD, THEN-SENATE MAJORITY LEADER MITCH MCCONNELL DECIDED TO BLOCK THE CANDIDATE FROM EVEN GETTING A CHANCE TO TALK TO CONGRESS, NEVER MIND VOTING FOR OR AGAINST HIM, AND KEPT THAT POSITION OPEN UNTIL HIS PREFERRED CANDIDATE, DONALD TRUMP, WAS PRESIDENT AND COULD NOMINATE WHO THEY WANTED. AND THAT IS THE ONLY REASON NEIL GORSUCH ENDED UP SITTING ON THE BENCH OF THE SUPREME COURT.

Per usual, the Supreme Court Justices remained stoic. During any State of the Union, the Justices have never been seen clapping, reacting, or even smiling if possible in order to not give the appearance of partisan politics. Despite polls showing that the public views the bench as having become highly politically divisive, the members themselves almost always attempt to present as neutral bodies. This is especially necessary since many policies announced during the State of the Union may end up in front of them. At that point, the President broke eye-contact with the Justices and shifted focus to the Majority Leader, saying:

LET ME BE CLEAR: WHAT MITCH MCCONNELL DID AND THE REST OF THE SENATE ALLOWED WAS A CRIME. HE KNOWINGLY LED A STRIKE AGAINST THE GOVERNMENT, WHICH WAS A VIOLATION OF THE OATH OF OFFICE. IF I WERE PRESIDENT THEN, I NEVER WOULD HAVE

ALLOWED THAT TO STAND AND WOULD HAVE
PLACED MCCONNELL UNDER ARREST. AND
IF WHOEVER REPLACED HIM REFUSED TO DO
THEIR JOB, I WOULD HAVE DONE THE SAME
TO THEM.

The unease was building, and many people in the room
peered down at the members of the Supreme Court to
gauge their reactions. Since they had none, everyone
turned back to the President who said:

SHOULD THIS CONGRESS PLAN TO DO
SOMETHING SIMILAR TO ME, I AM WARNING
YOU NOW THAT I WILL EXECUTE THE LAW AS
I AM REQUIRED TO DO PER MY OATH, AND I
WILL SEE YOU JAILED. YOU CAN VOTE
DOWN ALL MY NOMINEES, THAT IS FINE,
THAT IS YOUR RIGHT. BUT DON'T YOU DARE
BELIEVE FOR A MINUTE THAT I WILL ALLOW
YOU TO CIRCUMVENT THE LAWS OF THIS
GREAT NATION FOR YOUR OWN PERSONAL
AND/OR POLITICAL PARTY GAIN EVER
AGAIN.

Surprisingly, there was actually a smattering of applause
heard during this bombastic viciousness. Most was from the
President's own cabinet, but there was also a reaction
noted from the few fellow independents in Congress, as
well as some of the more extreme elements within the
Democratic and Republican Parties. Otherwise, there was
some mumbling and even a couple of "boos" were heard,
though their own colleagues seemed to shut those down
without the President or Speaker having to intervene.

PRESIDENT TRIED TO COOL THINGS DOWN AS TEMPERS FLARED

With most of Congress riled up and visibly upset, the President then attempted to change the cadence of the speech. Instead of digging in further, the President sought to raise the mood with a reminder that despite all the media hype and a perception that everything in the country is split fifty-fifty, there is actually much more agreement overall, even within the halls of the Capitol Building. As the President said:

> THE STORY THAT IS NEVER TOLD IS HOW MUCH THE MEMBERS OF CONGRESS HAVE IN COMMON WITH EACH OTHER, AND HOW OFTEN THEY AGREE. I TOOK A LOOK BACK AT THE 116TH CONGRESS THAT SERVED FROM JANUARY 3, 2019 TO JANUARY 3, 2021. IT WAS AS DIVIDED AS ANYONE COULD EXPECT OF OUR LEGISLATURE, WITH DEMOCRATS HOLDING A TINY MARGIN IN THE HOUSE OF REPRESENTATIVES AND REPUBLICANS HAVING THE SLIMMEST OF ADVANTAGES IN THE SENATE. AND THEN THE COVID-19 PANDEMIC HAPPENED, FOLLOWED BY A CONTENTIOUS ELECTION WHERE THE STANDING PRESIDENT DECLARED THE WHOLE THING A FARCE AND STIRRED UP AN ATTEMPTED COUP WITH THE ASSISTANCE OF MEMBERS FROM THIS VERY CHAMBER. TO SAY THAT PEOPLE WERE AT

EACH OTHER'S THROATS WAS NOT HYPER-
BOLE; IT WAS HAPPENING FOR REAL.

If this was the President's attempt at calming things down, it was not resonating. A number of those very members who lived through the described events are still representing their districts to this day, some having survived investigations by the then-Justice Department. However, the President brought it back to the main point:

 WHEN I LOOKED THROUGH ALL 344 BILLS THAT WERE PASSED AS LAW, I WAS SURPRISED TO SEE THAT 83% OF THE TIME THESE BILLS WERE APPROVED EITHER WITH UNANIMOUS CONSENT, WITHOUT OBJECTION, JUST WITH VOICE VOTE, OR MANY OTHER SIMILAR METHODS. BUT THIS IS THE REAL NARRATIVE HERE THAT IS NEVER REPORTED: THAT CONGRESS NOT ONLY DOES A LOT OF WORK TOGETHER, BUT DOES SO IN COMPLETE AGREEMENT. THERE IS NO REASON THAT THIS CANNOT BE CONGRESS' MESSAGE TO THE NATION, NOR ANY REASON THAT WE CANNOT DO THE SAME TOGETHER.

We fact-checked the statistics the President quoted and found them to be true, but in need of qualification. For instance, although that level of agreement does exist, over a fifth of the acts passed by Congress were for the naming of post offices alone—and that does not include branding other facilities. Most of what Congress did pass was mundane day-to-day operations and rather inconsequential.

Also, the President only looked at what became law; it did not include the plethora of bills that were passed by one chamber or the other and then there was no movement on them whatsoever, or the ones that involved both chambers and then still failed. Also, it must be noted that Representatives and Senators usually only introduce bills that they know are going to at least pass their own chamber. If the votes are not there, they do not even bother. This is the same reason for using tools like "voice vote", "without objection", and "unanimous consent"; it is known that the bill is going to pass because there are enough votes, so Representatives and Senators either do not want to get on record or do not want to bother with the paperwork.

EXECUTIVE BRANCH ATTEMPTS TO TELL JUDICIAL BRANCH HOW TO RUN

The President brought up similar measures for the results from the Supreme Court, noting how more often than not cases were decided unanimously and mostly did not fall on ideological lines. It was just when they have done so that it made the headlines and further inflamed partisan beliefs. At this point, the President did something never before seen during a State of the Union address: sign an Executive Order. Said the Commander-in-Chief:

ALTHOUGH THE PEOPLE IN THIS HALL ARE USED TO BEING THE ONES TO CREATE LEGAL PRECEDENT, I WOULD LIKE TO TRY MY HAND AT IT AS WELL.

With that, the President put pen to paper to bring the act into force. In this Executive Order, the President was making an argument for an approach the administration is calling the "Assessment of Harm" that is to be used when evaluating the validity of a law or Executive Order—the irony seemingly lost on the President. The leader of the free world has directed various law enforcement and quasi-court agencies that fall under the purview of the Executive Branch to consider whether a directive should be allowed to stand while going through objections based on a hierarchy. By that grading, the checks should go:

1. **People**
2. **Environment**
3. **Corporations and Organizations (including religious ones)**
4. **State Governments**
5. **The Federal Government**

In order words, if a new law is created and it is questionable whether there should be an injunction or not, the first check should see if it harms people, then the environment, and then the rest so that the Federal Government has the least consideration. It seems like a simple concept, but the court's current methods of making this assessment are quite opaque. Further, since the President cannot order the Judicial Branch to do anything, the Executive order only "recommends" that the Judicial Branch adopt the same guidance. That said, the President may be facing immediate pushback just by placing religion half-way down the list, especially given the current makeup of the Supreme Court.

SPEECH CLOSES OUT WITH DIRE ECONOMIC WARNING

This would be the only Executive Order the President gave

during the address. After that, the speech actually turned more "traditional" with the President laying out an intended agenda and various programs the White House would like to see Congress create or destroy.

We will be reviewing the key highlights in a set of forthcoming articles with important analysis from our team of political experts. Please return soon to see what the President plans to push Congress into doing next!

At the end of the speech, though, the President made one thing clear for the Representatives and Senators in the room. From this point forward, the President would only agree to continuing resolutions to keep the government open until September 30th, the end of the fiscal year. Anything that attempted to underwrite the government beyond that point would be vetoed, but so long as it stayed in that timeframe then the President would not disagree with the content. The President plainly stated that a 100% complete federal budget must be sent to the Oval Office for next fiscal year by that same date, otherwise the government would be shut down until one passed.

Before the President was inaugurated on January 20th and even prior to this Congress being sworn in on January 3rd, the prior Congress did pass several continuing resolutions. While much of the government is already funded until that September 30th date, some parts are only covered for the next several months. Democrats and Republicans basically bet that their own Party would be in complete control of Congress and the White House and that they could finalize their own agendas once they had settled in. Unfortunately for them, each chamber of Congress went to a different Party and the White House now sits in the hands of an independent who will not be making this accounting process easy for them.

Closing out the State of the Union, the President presented a prepared list of demands for the forthcoming budget that either must be met or there must be enough votes to override a veto. We will be discussing this in detail in an upcoming article, but suffice to say that with Congress as split as it is that there is not enough agreement to create a budget that could meet either of these situations. Still, there are over seven months before that deadline, so surely that is more than enough time for an appropriate and reasonable compromise to be found.

IS AMERICA ON THE CUSP OF A HEALTHCARE REVOLUTION?

PRESIDENT USES STATE OF THE UNION ADDRESS TO PROPOSE A VARIETY OF CHANGES TO THE ENTIRE MEDICAL SERVICES AND DELIVERY INDUSTRY

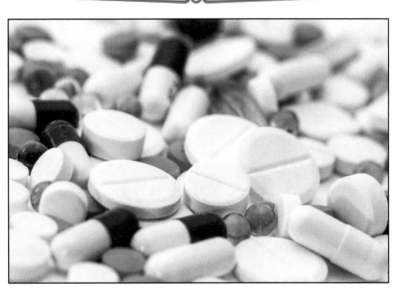

*An example of the expensive medicines that are a critical part of many Americans' lives. Photo by **PIXABAY**, CC0, via Wikimedia Commons.*

February 27th (Atlanta, GA) – Last night (February 26th), the President of the United States stood before a joint-session of Congress to deliver a rare first-year State of the Union Address. While those in attendance and the millions watching at home never learned if the condition of the country was "strong" or some other similar terminology, the President took the opportunity to lambast the Legislative and Judicial Branches for past perceived grievances. Yet after spending a good portion of the opening statement attacking these coequal parts of government, the President did take a significant amount of time to explain that there is usually more agreement than not, despite the rhetoric and the "media hype" of partisanship.

In that vein, the President then turned to an issue that has had a high level of agreement among the vast majority of Americans, yet has sunk the careers of many a politician: the cost of health care.

It is an indisputable fact that among western and developed countries, personal healthcare costs in the United States are many multiple of times more expensive than anywhere else comparable. Attempts have been made through legislation over the years to address the gaps in healthcare costs like with the creation of *Medicare* and *Medicaid* under President Lyndon B. Johnson, the *Affordable Care Act* under President Barack Obama, and the related components of the *Inflation Reduction Act* under President Joe Biden.

Yet none have been able to resolve the core issue.

A SINGLE TYLENOL PILL SHOULD NOT COST $15

In order to accomplish this seemingly impossible goal, the President has asked Congress to negotiate with the administration and develop a comprehensive plan that would lower the cost of healthcare using reasonable methods while leaving the private insurance and medical industry in place in order to appease concerns over "socialism". To explain this rather tall ambition, the President told the suspicious crowd:

LET ME BE CLEAR: THIS WILL NOT BE A PER-
FECT LAW. IT WILL NOT ENSURE EVERYONE
HAS PROPER CARE, IT WILL NOT CREATE A
SAFETY NET FOR EVERY AMERICAN, IT WILL
NOT STOP ALL CORPORATE GOUGING, AND—
MOST OF ALL—IT WILL NOT BE EVERYTHING
I WANT. HOWEVER, IT IS A STARTING
POINT, A SEEDLING TO BUILD AND GROW
UPON. WE BEGIN WITH SMALL FOUNDA-
TIONAL AGREEMENTS AND THEN ADD
BRICKS TO THAT BASE AS WE UNCOVER IS-
SUES WITH OUR APPROACH.

To that end, the leader of the free world presented something that the White House considers "low hanging fruit"
which could easily be solved by legislation, a resolution that
should have wide agreement:

ACCORDING TO RECENT STUDIES, THE "AV-
ERAGE" COST OF A SINGLE PILL OF TYLENOL
IN A HOSPITAL IS $15. AND THAT IS AVER-
AGE! LOOKING AT THE RAW DATA, THERE
ARE EXAMPLES OF HOSPITALS CHARGING
TEN TIMES THAT AMOUNT. AND IT DOES
NOT STOP THERE. LITTLE PLASTIC CUPS FOR
PILLS AVERAGE $10, ALCOHOL SWABS $23
A PIECE, AND EACH PAIR OF GLOVES COMES
IN AT AN UNBELIEVABLE $53!

This, the President contends, is one of the core reasons
that healthcare is so expensive. In order to eliminate

"unreasonable markup", the President has proposed legislation that would not allow hospitals or other medical institutions to charge a markup at all on medical and disposable equipment; instead they would only be allowed to pass on the actual costs to the consumers. Or, if Congress thinks a zero-dollar markup is unreasonable, cap it at a small percentage, like one to two percent. That would mean a single pill of Tylenol would cost $0.05 per capsule with no markup (when purchased in bulk) and maybe $0.06 if there were an allowed 10% markup (rounding up to the nearest whole cent).

As the President spoke, the idea was laid out as a compromise unto itself. The proposal was not asking for price controls on the production side, just that consumers pay what they would outside a medical setting, a fairness that is covered under the Commerce Clause of the Constitution and is in line with existing Federal and State laws on price gouging. The President asked Congress to pass this "common sense" legislation as a stand-alone piece and bring it to the Resolute Desk in the Oval Office where it would promptly be signed into law, unless, as the President cautioned those in attendance:

 [Y]OU BELIEVE HOSPITALS SHOULD BE ALLOWED TO RIP OFF YOUR CONSTITUENTS AND PUT THEM INTO INSURMOUNTABLE DEBT, ALL WHILE LINING THEIR OWN POCKETS. GO AHEAD, ASK YOUR VOTERS WHAT THEY THINK ABOUT THIS. OR, IF YOU DON'T HAVE THE TIME, MY ADMINISTRATION WOULD BE MORE THAN HAPPY TO DO IT FOR YOU AND REPORT THE RESULTS.

MEDICAL BILLING SHOULD BE CLEAR

After that veiled threat, the President called that potential piece of legislation the "medical cornerstone" and stated that others could be passed over time to build on the momentum of "agreement and reason." Up next in that category, the President recommended legislation around transparent billing. Medical billing has always been a black hole of incomprehensible levels, multiple providers charging from the same facility, and just plain surprises. The President did not have a plan ready for any of this, but did have a couple of specific suggestions.

First, the President wanted to see line items to easily explain every little bit a person was charged for, especially a breakout between the cost of items that are used and the cost of service, similar to what one would expect on a home or car repair project. Further, the President would like to see those items listed with multiple columns showing the direct cost to the hospital, the charge to consumers, what was paid by insurance, and what still remained. This would, the President argued, give consumers a base-level understanding and ability to file disputes with the necessary detail instead of the opaque bills they currently receive.

While that idea may be palatable to most members of Congress, the next suggestion was sure to lose a large percentage of them. For this, the President made a recommendation that Congress empower an existing or new Federal Agency or board to set the service rates that medical institutions could even charge to begin with. In support of this argument, the President said that almost all States do something similar with energy rates right now—where utility companies have to get approval from a board of governance to change tolls. Said the President:

IF ENERGY DELIVERY IS A COMMODITY AND A LOCAL-AREA MONOPOLY THAT THE GOVERNMENT FEELS IT MUST GET INVOLVED IN TO PROTECT CONSUMERS, THEN IS NOT HEALTHCARE THE SAME THING? IS THERE A LARGE, DIVERSE MARKET TO MAKE A SELECTION FROM, OR DO MOST PEOPLE JUST HAVE ONE OPTION NEARBY? DURING AN EMERGENCY SITUATION, WHILE RIDING IN AN AMBULANCE, IS SOMEONE REALLY GOING TO BE SHOPPING FOR AN EQUIVALENT HOSPITAL A HUNDRED MILES AWAY AND COMPARE PRICES?

This, though, would certainly not be the most controversial proposal the President made that evening.

No Company Involved in Healthcare Should be For-Profit

The award for legislation least likely to see the light of day went to the President's next pitch. Here, the President asked why medical institutions—especially drug makers— were allowed to be for-profit companies at all. Instead, the President proposed a radical idea that all of those organizations should be forced into becoming non-profits. In particular, the President felt that even if not involuntarily compelled into being non-profits, drug companies should face a similar pass-through requirement like hospitals and other medical institutions where they could only charge for the direct costs of manufacturing and distribution, plus whatever markup Congress deemed appropriate. The basic idea was that the base ingredients that go into drugs should not be up charged to consumers, at least not by much.

As if that was not enough of a push outside Congress's comfort zone, the President then proposed the idea that the Federal Government should fund and create its own drug-development company, or at a minimum create a board to oversee a fund that would distribute research and development (R&D) dollars to private companies to do the work for the government. The President also argued that if the Federal Government owned a manufacturing company for generic drugs—medications that have fallen off patent and can be made by anyone—then the agency would be self-funding, like many of the banking ones or the Post Office. Said the President:

OVER THE PAST FEW YEARS, WE HAVE SEEN SOME LIMITED SUCCESS IN CALIFORNIA AND SEVERAL OTHER STATES AS THEY HAVE CREATED A NASCENT INDUSTRY OF STATE-OWNED GENERIC DRUG MANUFACTURERS FOR A FEW SPECIFIC MEDICINES, LIKE INSULIN. THEY HAVE PROVEN THAT THE IDEA IS SOUND, BUT TO TRULY TAKE OFF IT NEEDS THE FORCE, FUNDING, AND BOLDNESS THAT ONLY THE FEDERAL GOVERNMENT CAN PROVIDE.

And, as the President argued, it would not be that far outside what the country already does with funding research in areas like cancer, strokes, and other conditions to the tune of $250 billion per year. However, the President even took umbrage with how those dollars were spent.

RESOURCES SHOULD GO TOWARDS THE REAL #1 KILLER OF AMERICANS

 WHAT IF I TOLD YOU ABOUT SOMETHING THAT KILLED OVER 700,000 AMERICANS IN THE LAST 12 MONTHS ALONE, AND IN THE NEXT 12 MONTHS WILL KILL EVEN MORE? ON TOP OF THAT, WHAT IF YOU KNEW THAT THE NUMBER OF DEATHS WILL ONLY CONTINUE TO INCREASE EVERY SINGLE YEAR, WITH NO SIGNS OF IT ABATING? IS THIS NOT THE DEFINITION OF A CRISIS, AN EMERGENCY THAT NEEDS TO BE ADDRESSED?

These words began the President's finale in the healthcare-portion of the State of the Union. Here, the President highlighted that, according to every study, **heart disease** has consistently remained the top killer of Americans by a wide margin. Further, the President said that this epidemic grows in severity every subsequent year due to Americans' overall unhealthy lifestyle choices combined with a lack of affordable and readily available support services. Yet, when compared to the United States' total investment in research and development in the prior year, the dollars earmarked towards treating heart disease amounted to less than 1% of the funding allocated by Congress. The President additionally highlighted that funding to help prevent the top ten killers of Americans only accounted for 10% of medical research spending by the government, while basic clinical research by itself accounted for over 6% of those monies.

As the President expounded:

AND THIS IS ONLY WHAT THE FEDERAL GOVERNMENT IS DIRECTLY SPENDING ON MEDICAL RESEARCH, AND DOESN'T INCLUDE WHERE WE WASTE OUR MONEY ELSEWHERE THAT IS NOT SPENT ON SAVING LIVES. WE EXPEND AROUND $150 BILLION ON ANTI-TERRORISM RELATED ACTIVITIES AND ONLY $2 BILLION ON PREVENTING HEART DIS-EASE. BUT TERRORISM ONLY KILLS 300 PEOPLE A YEAR. YOU HAVE A GREATER CHANCE OF DYING FROM SUNSTROKE THAN THAT!

The President did admit that without some level of funding, deaths from terrorism would be higher, so the administration was not proposing that those programs be completely defunded; just that apportionments should be rebalanced in a way that makes sense. However, even if deaths from terrorism were ten times higher, it would amount to only 2,700 additional deaths; meaning that the cost of saving those people was currently pegged at $56 million per person. Said the President:

DO YOU THINK IT WOULD COST $56 MIL-LION TO SAVE ONE PERSON FROM HEART DISEASE, CANCER, OR THE FLU? IF THAT SOUNDS COLD-HEARTED TO THE PERSON WHO IS KILLED, THAT IS WHAT IT MEANS TO USE EMPIRICAL STATISTICAL ANALYSIS TO MAKE CRITICAL DECISIONS.

Here was the crux of what the President was proposing. Instead of relying on emotional responses and focusing on the squeakiest wheel, the President wanted Congress to create a funding model that was based on statistics alone. That way, it would not be a political question, it would just be one based on which dollars would get the greatest return on investment; that return being people saved.

With this, the President wrapped up the medical portion of the State of the Union. But that was only a subsection of what the President wanted for funding all scientific research and endeavors. For that, the Commander-in-Chief had another multiple-part vision that is awaiting its own meme like the *Ten Pronouncements*.

CLIMATE CHANGE IS A SECURITY ISSUE, PRESIDENT INSISTS

STATE OF THE UNION ADDRESSES KEY TOPICS RELATED TO WATER, ENERGY, ELECTRIC CARS, CARBON, AND... A SPACE ELEVATOR?

This lonely windmill will not be enough to power all of the President's ideas. Photo by @SAGE_SOLAR FROM CHICHESTER, UNITED KINGDOM, CC BY 2.0, Public Domain via Wikimedia Commons.

February 27th (Newport News, VA) – The President wants the country to focus in on five very specific scientific endeavors; ones that the administration says will tackle "the current real security problems and human toll due to climate change", but will also set the United States up for a long-term future. By attempting to frame these issues both as "security" and "climate change", the President seems to be hoping to woo enough Republicans and

Democrats into supporting a common cause, even if it is for entirely different reasons.

During the State of the Union address, the President had already spent a good deal of time talking about healthcare yet was not done asking Congress to take more bold leaps. In this case, though, instead of trying to make massive changes across an entire embedded industry, the President expressed the need for America to concentrate its efforts on a few scant ideas that would make the most impact. The premise was definitively around environmentalism, for the most part, even though the last suggestion was for an elevator into space.

WATER, WATER EVERYWHERE, NE'ER A DROP TO DRINK

At the top of the agenda was what the President called "Water Security". By the Commander-in-Chief's reasoning, there is enough water in the United States and the entire world, it is just distributed incorrectly. For instance, States like Florida are completely drenched in water and have already seen the dangers of coastal erosion and internal displacement related to rising sea levels as the ice caps have melted. Meanwhile, in southwest States like Arizona, being dependent upon water allocations from the Colorado River had proved impossible to maintain by the early 2020s as snowfall that fed the waterway dramatically decreased. Both of these issues, the President said, can be solved with the same solution: desalination plants and piping networks.

Desalination is the process of removing salt and other contaminants from ocean water and turning it into a potable form for human consumption and use. The President would like to see immense desalination plants built on the coasts—plants that would run solely on renewable sources—and pump that water to pools in the deserts and water-strapped areas of the United States. More so, the President would like to have this program expanded to overseas, even potentially creating the largest freshwater lake in the world in the middle of the Sahara Desert. Said the President:

THE NUMBER ONE REASON COUNTRIES ARE AND WILL BE GOING TO WAR IS FOR CONTROL OVER RESOURCES, ESPECIALLY FRESH WATER, THE COMPOUND THAT IS ESSENTIAL FOR ALL LIFE. NOW IMAGINE JUST MAKING WATER AN ABUNDANT RESOURCE FOR A MINOR INVESTMENT. AND LET'S DO SOME BASIC MATH—WHICH IS MORE EXPENSIVE: ANOTHER ENDLESS WAR OR STOPPING WAR BEFORE IT EVEN STARTS WITH A GLASS OF H_2O?

The President argued that this would kill not just two birds with one stone, but "a whole flock of them". Desalination on a massive global scale would stop and reverse sea level rise, ending a potential refugee situation for the 40% of the world population that currently lives in the flood zones of the coast. At the same time, it would provide a much-needed supply of fresh water that is necessary for consumption and farming, creating food security in places that have not had it in all of modern human history. However, the President was not unaware of critics that say using desalination is dangerous and may pose a risk to ocean life. In response to those groups, the President stated:

> WE HAVE SEVERAL IMMEDIATE AND PERILOUS DIFFICULTIES WE NEED TO SOLVE NOW. BECAUSE OF THAT, THERE ARE GOING TO BE TRADEOFFS. WE CAN WORK TO MITIGATE THOSE ISSUES AND MAYBE, SOMEDAY IN THE FUTURE, WE WILL BE ABLE TO TURN OFF THE SPIGOTS. BUT WE HAVE TO ADDRESS THE REALITY OF THE ONGOING IMPACTS OF CLIMATE CHANGE FIRST WHILE WE WORK TOWARDS HAVING A FUTURE WHEN THESE MEASURES WILL NO LONGER BE NEEDED. UNFORTUNATELY, THAT IS A MULTI-GENERATIONAL AFFAIR, NOT SOMETHING NEARLY QUICK ENOUGH TO SAVE MANKIND.

That said, the President did submit ideas that should be implemented along with this desalination program to address long-term concerns. Many of these were just expansions of successful programs seen in water-starved areas like California, Israel, the United Arab Emirates, and others that seemingly just "lacked the willpower" to be implemented around the country and the rest of the world. These included, but were not limited to:

- In agriculture, using recycled grey water (previously used water from things like showers and toilets that has been mildly treated) in direct drip irrigation instead of free spraying water from overhead;

- In reservoirs, rivers, and other water transports, covering them with solar panels to minimize evaporation while also generating electricity for the pumps;

- In the home, installing low-flow shower heads and faucets that make people feel like they are getting the same water pressure while actually cutting usage by up to 70%.

Again, the President recognized that the most hawkish proponents of addressing Climate Change head-on would want to modify behavior first to get people to take shorter showers, but the President found this approach unrealistic. To this, the President declared:

 YOU HAVE TO MEET PEOPLE WHERE THEY ARE AND, REALISTICALLY, THIS IS WHERE THEY ARE AT.

IT'S ELECTRIC, BOOGIE WOOGIE, WOOGIE

This same idea of not waiting decades to change attitudes and actions carried through into the next area entitled "Energy Diversification". Not unexpectedly, the President suggested a colossal expansion into solar, wind, wave, geothermal, and every other non-emitting energy source. To the surprise of many, though, the President stated a desire to not just build more nuclear power plants, but to actually recycle existing and future nuclear waste.

According to a 2022 study by the **Idaho National Laboratory**, at that time there was already enough nuclear waste left over from reactors "to power the entire country for 100 years." Technology to do so is well known, having been vetted for over 30 years starting in the 1960s. Other nuclear powers like Russia also successfully implemented this technology and maintain it to this day. Congress in the past even supported one of these so-called "Fast Reactors" before shutting it down by eliminating funding due to the political pressures of that era.

The President sees that decision as an egregious mistake of a prior administration and wants to catch up on lost time and knowledge. That said, even if Congress were to fund the creation of these plants and somehow hope to find the economies of scale necessary to bring the price down enough for widespread commercial use later, that would still take years, if not decades. Since that type of plan would seemingly go against the urgency the President was portending, another strategy was needed for the here-and-now.

With this, the President said the best thing we could do is require every rooftop in America to be filled with solar panels and storage batteries. The President proposed a public-private partnership where real estate and home owners could choose to purchase the panels themselves and reap all the benefits of net metering (utility companies being forced to buy all the energy that is produced and sent into the grid); let a private company pay and create some type of revenue sharing and lease deal; or have the government do the installation under a program that would see the majority of benefits go directly to itself, at least until the government recouped its investment plus interest. As the President said:

 IF WE HAVE AN OVERABUNDANCE OF ELECTRICITY, IT WILL FORCE PRICES DOWN TO THE POINT WHERE FOSSIL FUELS WILL NOT

EVEN BE ABLE TO COMPETE. ADDITIONALLY, WE NEED TO HAVE PROGRAMS TO TURN ALL HOME AND BUILDING HVAC SYSTEMS INTO ELECTRIC ONES THROUGH REBATES AND DISCOUNT INSTALLATIONS, PERHAPS EVEN UP TO 100%. IN ORDER TO END OUR ADDICTION TO FOSSIL FUELS, THE REPLACEMENTS MUST FEEL EXACTLY THE SAME AND PROVIDE A NOTICEABLE BENEFIT, OTHERWISE PEOPLE WILL CONTINUE TO CLING TO OLD AND UNSUSTAINABLE WAYS.

BABY, YOU CAN DRIVE MY CAR

Yet, when it comes to controlling emissions from burning fossil fuels, a significant factor had been left out of the discussion up to this point: automobiles. According to the formerly independent **Environmental Protection Agency** (EPA), nearly a sixth of all carbon-contribution comes directly from people driving around in their passenger and light-duty vehicles. If adding in the rest of "transportation", that amount doubles.

The obvious solution that could be coupled with the President's other plans would be to expand the availability of electric vehicles. This could be done by banning the building of new combustion engines after a certain time (as some States have attempted) and/or providing discount and trade-in tax rebates to accelerate the uptake of new vehicles that meet the necessary standards. And for sure, the President did recommend those very programs, but was less forceful than normal, saying there was another problem that needed to be handled first:

 WE HAVE A CART-BEFORE-THE-HORSE IS-SUE TO RESOLVE BEFORE ANY OF THAT. CRITICS OF AN ALL-ELECTRIC FLEET WILL HIGHLIGHT THAT LIQUID FUELS GET BETTER EFFICIENCIES ON A MILES-PER-ENERGY BA-SIS, AND THAT A CHARGING STATION TAKES FAR LONGER THAN JUST FILLING UP. IF CHARGING IS NOT AT LEAST AS EASY AND CONVENIENT AS FILLING UP AT THE GAS STATION, THEN CONSUMERS WILL NOT ADOPT THE CHANGE TO ELECTRIC VEHICLES. WE HAVE ALREADY SEEN THIS IN OUR PRIOR ATTEMPTS AT EXPANDING THE ELEC-TRIC-VEHICLE INFRASTRUCTURE.

The President then discussed the naysayers some more, going deeper into what had already been done:

 EVEN WHEN COMBINING THE IMPACT FROM THE *INFRASTRUCTURE INVESTMENT AND JOBS ACT OF 2021* AND THE *INFLATION REDUCTION ACT OF 2022* PASSED BY THIS CONGRESS UNDER PRESIDENT JOE BIDEN, THERE ARE STILL MASSIVE GAPS WHERE PEOPLE CANNOT GO THE DISTANCES NEEDED BETWEEN CHARGING LOCATIONS BASED ON CURRENT TECHNOLOGY. AND ALTHOUGH THE VAST MAJORITY OF PEOPLE USUALLY ONLY GO A FEW MILES IN A DAY AND CAN

CHARGE AT HOME, JUST THE THOUGHT OF
THIS POSSIBILITY HAS HINDERED THE UP-
TAKE IN ALL-ELECTRIC VEHICLES.

At this pronouncement, the thought was that the President was going to recommend more investment into that same infrastructure, as well as using government monies to fund research into increasing the range of vehicles. Conversely, the President proposed a novel approach, but one that will require an enormous retooling of the entire automotive industry.

Here, the President said that the batteries that power vehicles should—under a government program—become completely standardized. Then, each manufacturer would be required to use that standard battery and make them easily accessible, preferably under the hood. Finally, these batteries would be able to be disconnected and replaced with ease. By the President's vision, current gas station attendants would provide this service so that when a car was running low on charge, it could just pull into a gas station where they would do a quick swap out in a couple of minutes. Said the President:

 I IMAGINE THIS MORE LIKE PROPANE TANKS FOR GRILLS THAT WE HAVE NOW. WHEN I RUN OUT OF GAS, I JUST BRING IT TO ANY NUMBER OF LOCATIONS AND PAY A FEE TO SWITCH IT OUT. THEY DON'T FILL MY TANK; THEY GIVE ME ANOTHER ONE THEY FILLED EARLIER. THE STANDARD EMPTY TANK I DROPPED OFF WILL THEN BE FILLED UP SOMETIME LATER AND SOLD TO SOMEONE

ELSE. **I**F CAR BATTERIES WERE LIKE THIS, THEN OUR ISSUES WOULD BE RESOLVED; OR AT LEAST THE PSYCHOLOGICAL HANG-UP ONES AROUND CHARGING TIMES, WHETHER OR NOT THOSE CONCERNS ARE BASED IN RE-ALITY.

What the President intends to do about propane tanks (or charcoal, for that matter) was left unsaid.

▌FROM THE REDWOOD FOREST TO THE GULF STREAM WATERS

Of course, all this discussion of major environmental and energy programs would cover the long-term future of getting to a zero-emissions society, but it did not tackle the damage that has already been done. Included in the *Infrastructure Investment and Job Act of 2021* that the President referenced earlier in the speech were billions of dollars for "carbon capture" technology to remove harmful greenhouse-gas-trapping particulates from the air. In May 2022, the Biden administration announced the launch of a $2.3 billion pilot program. After the announcement, the then-Secretary of the **Department of Energy** (now a component of the Executive Division of **Science, Technology, and Environment**) Jennifer Granholm told CNBC in a video interview (*https://www.cnbc.com/2022/05/08/energy-secretary-why-feds-are-spending-2point5-billion-on-carbon-capture.html*):

THERE'S CRITICISM THAT SOMETHING LIKE THIS—CARBON CAPTURE AND SEQUESTRA-TION—MERELY PROLONGS ASSETS THAT

THE FOSSIL INDUSTRY WOULD BE USING...
I WILL SAY THIS: ANYTHING WE CAN DO TO
DECARBONIZE IS A GOOD THING.

Earlier in the same interview, Ms. Granholm discussed the naysayers who did not see the value of carbon capture and only wanted to see mass changes where fossil fuel use would be completely eliminated:

> **CERTAINLY, OUR FIRST PREFERENCE IS TO MAKE SURE THAT WE ARE POWERED BY CLEAN, ZERO CARBON EMITTING ENERGY. AND WE'RE DOING ALL OF THAT. BUT YOU CAN WALK AND CHEW GUM [AT THE SAME TIME]...**

Based on early results, the technology showed great promise. Nevertheless, the price of sequestering carbon did not come down fast enough to become economically feasible, and Congress never reached another agreement to fund the program for additional years. Today, just a handful of these plants are in operation and they are not doing nearly enough to make the necessary impact.

Here, the President asked Congress to fund this program again. Specifically, the President referenced the very successful—but controversial—public-private partnership the government had with ExxonMobil. While it was proven as a concept, many liberal environmentalists could not reconcile efforts to rescue the world by giving money to the companies that had partaken in destroying it. This led to enough Democrats withholding their support so that the Party could not even get any carbon-capture legislation through a reconciliation process. This President appeared to be much more pragmatic in the ask:

I DON'T CARE ABOUT THE MOTIVATIONS BEHIND BIG ENERGY COMPANIES LIKE EXXONMOBIL. I UNDERSTAND THIS IS LIKE A CIGARETTE COMPANY SELLING SMOKING SECESSION PRODUCTS—WHICH THEY DO, BY THE WAY. ALL THAT MATTERS IS THE END RESULTS; AND IF THE PEOPLE AND COMPANIES THAT GOT US INTO THIS MESS IN TURN HELP GET US OUT OF IT, THEN SO BE IT. IF WE END UP PAYING THESE ORGANIZATIONS TO CLEAN UP THE DISASTER THEY CREATED, IT IS THE BITTER PILL WE WILL HAVE TO SWALLOW BECAUSE WE NEED TO DO THIS. FORGET YOUR PRIDE, FORGET YOUR DESIRE FOR JUSTICE OR VENGEANCE—THOSE THINGS WILL NOT SAVE THE WORLD.

Despite this plea for corporate forgiveness in the name of the greater good, the President did suggest other methodologies that should also be implemented concurrently, including the planting of trees as well as growing native species on the edges of farmlands.

AND I THINK IT'S GONNA BE A LONG, LONG TIME

Wrapping up the section of the State of the Union focused on the sciences, the President took a sudden U-turn out of environmentalism and into astrophysics. That said, the

President did at least attempt to bridge the themes:

> WHEN WE TALK ABOUT GROWING INDUS-
> TRIES THAT ARE HEAVY POLLUTERS AND
> DOING SIGNIFICANT DAMAGE TO THE
> PLANET, I WOULD BE REMISS NOT TO BRING
> UP THE COMMERCIALIZATION OF SPACE.
> PRIVATE AND PUBLIC ROCKETS ARE
> LAUNCHING THROUGH THE IONOSPHERE AT
> A RATE OF HUNDREDS A YEAR, DOING REAL
> DAMAGE THAT IMPACTS US BACK ON EARTH.
> AND THAT DOES NOT EVEN GET INTO THE
> BURNING OF ROCKET FUELS, THE GROUND
> CONTAMINATION, AND THE LITERAL ACTION
> OF BLASTING RARE EARTH ELEMENTS OFF
> THE PLANET TO NEVER BE SEEN AGAIN.

The President stressed that the administration was not against the commercialization or exploration of outer space—even though no aliens were found at **Area 51** during the President's earlier visit there. What the White House was proposing was that because the United States already has so many private partners to help get the country's astronauts to our space stations and to do scientific missions, it was time for NASA to accomplish a much larger goal.

Calling it "this millennia's moonshot", the President brought up the idea of an elevator into space that would eliminate the need for rocketry all together while providing a clean and reliable way to get to the cosmos on a regular basis, opening it up for true utilization. This would start with tourism, then evolve into industrialization and, finally, colonization—even to unexpected places like in the clouds above the sky on Venus.

The idea of a space elevator is not new. Without getting into the engineering or mechanics, basically a long line would be tied down somewhere on Earth and a counterweight would be put out beyond the atmosphere. The rotation of the planet alone would be enough to keep the line taut, and then baskets could slowly ascend and descend using renewable energy sources.

While theoretically possible, all limited academic research to date shows that there is no material currently available—whether naturally occurring or man-made—that would work on Earth. Interestingly, though, such materials do exist that would fit the bill on smaller astral bodies like the Moon and Mars. Thus, the concept could be tested as part of the ongoing *Project Artemis* on the Moon and/or in the forthcoming Martian missions. Still, the cost to produce those materials right now is astronomical, so to speak.

As such, it seems what the President was really asking for here was the investment into futuristic materials that can be used for the space elevator and many other purposes. Further, the President found this would be a chance for diplomacy as the best places on Earth to situate a space elevator were certainly not within the borders or territories of the United States:

 SUCH AN ENDEAVOR REQUIRES US TO WORK COOPERATIVELY WITH COUNTRIES ALL OVER THIS PLANET, WHETHER THEY ARE OUR ALLIES ARE NOT. AS I SAID DURING MY INAUGURATION, I AM NOT AGAINST INTERNATIONALISM, JUST THE INSTITUTIONS

THAT HAVE FAILED IN THEIR MISSION OF KEEPING PEACE ON EARTH AND HAVE BEEN IRREPARABLY CORRUPTED. WE DO NOT NEED THE U.N. TO BUILD A SPACE ELEVATOR ON VOLCÁN CAYAMBE IN ECUADOR; WE NEED THE AGREEMENT OF ECUADOR AND THEIR NEIGHBORS, AND HELP FROM OUR TRUSTED PARTNERS LIKE THE E.U., JAPAN, AND CANADA.

Still, despite all of these far-reaching ideals, some people expressed extreme disappointment in the President. Many were expecting the President to close out this section by declaring Climate Change a "national emergency" and unlocking funds to accomplish at least some of these proposals. Much to their chagrin, those dreams were dashed as for once the President chose not to make any commandments, but only pleaded with Congress to take action—action they have failed to take for time immemorial.

HIGH SCHOOL GRADUATES NOT EQUIPPED FOR "ADULTING", PRESIDENT SAYS

WHITE HOUSE PROPOSES MANDATORY "TWO YEARS OF SERVICE" FOR EVERY YOUNG PERSON

Rough stones graduate into the world, unprepared for what lies ahead in "real life". Photo by WOKANDAPIX, CC0, via Wikimedia Commons.

February 27ᵗʰ (Providence, RI) – Are 18-year-olds ready for college and starting down the path to their professional lives? The President of the United States does not believe so.

Last night (February 26ᵗʰ) during the State of the Union, the President spoke to a joint session of Congress and presented a wide-ranging array of policies and proposals.

Education, in particular, seems to be a key concern of the White House. Earlier in the month on February 9th, the President signed an Executive Order attempting to redefine what "post-secondary education" even means. In that text, the President stated a desire to have non-traditional paths be considered equivalent to having a college degree, especially those in the trades field. However, based upon the speech last night, the President has broader ideas about when those scholastic pursuits should take place.

A New "Selective Service" for Everyone to Discover Themselves

The President began talking about education stating:

> WE CAN QUIBBLE OVER THE EXACT STATISTICS—AND I'M SURE THE FACT CHECK WEBSITES WILL—BUT ONLY AROUND HALF OF THE PEOPLE WHO ATTEMPT TO GET A BACHELOR'S DEGREE EVER DO. THAT MEANS THEY TAKE ON ALL THAT DEBT, ALL THAT RESPONSIBILITY, AND ALL THOSE CONSEQUENCES, AND HAVE NOTHING TO SHOW FOR IT.

With this, the President asked the members of Congress how many of them knew what they wanted to do with their lives right out of high school. The speech then turned to discussions of the modern understanding of psychology and neurological development, with the President arguing that "it is simply too early for these kids" to make such momentous decisions that are going to impact them for several subsequent decades, at the very least.

As such, the President recommended Congress instead create a "compulsory service program" that would last for a period of two years. This service would begin on August 1st of the year after someone had completed their secondary education—no matter if they graduated, got a GED or equivalent, or dropped out earlier—and had turned 18 years of age. If they had a birthday later than August 1st or were still actively working to complete their secondary education, then their start date could be delayed by several months and they could come in together as an "off cycle class". The President contended that this would be a natural extension of the *Selective Service System*, which already requires young people to sign up for a potential military draft; though no one has been required to serve in this manner since the 1970s. Further, the President highlighted that the Supreme Court has found multiple times that *Selective Service* and the draft are completely Constitutional, so long as it is evenly applied, the workers are fairly compensated, and the episode has a time limit. The President expanded on this idea, saying in part:

 AND I AM NOT TALKING ABOUT HAVING EVERYONE DO DIRECT, FRONT-LINE COMBAT MILITARY DUTY, EITHER; UNLESS THEY WANT TO DO THAT. IN COUNTRIES LIKE NORWAY, SOUTH KOREA, ISRAEL, BRAZIL, AND OTHERS, THE MAJORITY OF PEOPLE WORK IN ADMINISTRATIVE ROLES... TODAY'S ARMED FORCES ARE PEACEKEEPERS, TECHNOLOGISTS, BUILDERS, AND SO MUCH MORE. WE CAN LET THESE EMERGING ADULTS TRY OUT ONE OR ANY NUMBER OF ROLES, PUTTING THEM ON ROTATIONS AND

GIVING THEM EXPOSURE AND EXPERIENCES
TO DISCOVER WHO THEY ARE AND WHAT
THEY ARE INTERESTED IN, ALL BEFORE MOV-
ING ON TO FURTHER EDUCATION—
WHATEVER THAT MAY MEAN TO THEM. IN
THE INTERIM, WHILE THEY LEARN AND
GROW, THE COUNTRY WILL ALSO BENEFIT
FROM THEIR LABOR. AND PERHAPS WE WILL
DISCOVER A FEW EXCEPTIONAL CANDI-
DATES THAT MAY WANT TO CONTINUE IN
HIGHER LEVELS OF GOVERNMENT SERVICE.

The President even brought up the possibility of people being able to work for a non-profit organization of their choice
while on the payroll of the United States federal government. At this point, the President did not outline how the
country could possibly afford to pay for such a program but
hinted at ideas that focused on reallocating military funds
and other revenue-generating measures. It would not be
until later that the President would give an overview of the
administration's expectations in regard to the entire federal
budget.

Back on the subject of government-sponsored vassalage,
the President noted that almost 40% of countries around
the world already have a required conscription and/or vol-
unteerism, and another 10%—including America—have a
"du jure" draft in the form of Selective Service that is currently not being enforced. That, of course, does not take
into account the other half of the world that lacks any type
of forced servitude, nor that many countries are actually
rolling back these requirements. In 2020, the aforementioned South Korea passed what some have dubbed the

"BTS Law" (named for the K-pop band popular at the time) that allowed "globally relevant entertainers" to defer their service until they turned 30.

PRESIDENT USES PROPS TO TRY TO CHANGE OUTLOOKS

During the education component of the State of the Union, the President also tried another "reset of expectations." To make a point, the President set up a visual aid with a wastepaper basket being placed some distance away and then attempted to land a crumpled-up piece of paper in it. After missing several shots to some chuckles, the President told the crowd:

MOST OF US HAVE HEARD OF THIS EXAMPLE OF INEQUALITY, WHERE THOSE CLOSER TO THE BASKET CAN MAKE THE SHOT MORE EASILY. HOWEVER, I THINK ANOTHER IMPORTANT SUBJECT HAS BEEN MISSED: THE LOCATION OF THE BASKET. WHERE IT SITS RIGHT NOW IS BEING A POINT GUARD IN THE NBA, A SOCIAL MEDIA STAR, A GENIUS INVENTOR, A LOTTERY WINNER, OR EVEN PRESIDENT OF THE UNITED STATES.

This self-deprecating humor seemed to win over a few more people in the crowd, especially considering how the State of the Union began. The President had come out incredibly hostile towards the members of Congress and had already spent a great deal of time trying to lower the tension that had been created by those words.

After air-balling and bricking a few more shots, the President continued:

WHILE THESE ARE NOBLE GOALS, THEY ARE NOT REALISTIC FOR EVERYONE. IF EVERYBODY IS AIMING FOR THE TOP, THEN MOST PEOPLE ARE GOING TO MISS. INSTEAD, MAYBE WE SHOULD MOVE THE BASKET CLOSER.

At this, the President did exactly that, and finally made a shot with more ease.

THIS IS CHANGING EXPECTATION FROM ALWAYS SHOOTING FOR THE "BEST" TO GOING FOR "GOOD". SURE, PEOPLE WILL STILL MISS THIS, BUT FAR FEWER WILL, AND WE CAN BETTER SUPPORT THEM WHEN THEY DO BECAUSE OUR RESOURCES WILL NOT BE STRETCHED AS THIN. AND YES, THE "BEST" WILL STILL FIND A WAY TO RISE TO THE TOP; I AM NOT SUGGESTING WE HOLD BACK EXCELLENCE FOR "FAIRNESS" OR ANY SUCH THING.

Whether the President's dog and pony show was able to get through to Congress remains to be seen.

THE END OF DELAWARE BEING A TAX HAVEN FINALLY AT HAND?

PRESIDENT PROPOSES ELIMINATING LOOPHOLE THAT ALLOWS COMPANIES TO AVOID PAYING THEIR TAXES

Outside the Corporation Trust Center in Wilmington, DE, which is the home to over 6,500 public companies and the address of almost 300,000 businesses. Photo and modified description by DAVIDT8, Public Domain, via Wikimedia Commons.

February 27th (Wilmington, DE) – During the State of the Union, the President asked Congress to "close the Delaware Loophole" and level the playing field between States for attracting and retaining businesses.

Background: *The Delaware General Corporation Law*—as the directive that contains the loophole is officially known— allows companies to evade taxes on "intangible assets". This includes items like patents, trademarks, copyrights, and other "goodwill", i.e., the value of the brand name. Additionally, this could encompass possessions like electronic databases, notably financial systems and customer lists. Basically, whatever is not "tangible", such as land, a building, equipment, or any other physical possessions.

More benefits: There are a host of other potential advantages, including companies being able to charge themselves royalties and not pay taxes on those fees. For instance, McDonalds keeps their trademarks in Delaware and bills their franchises and corporate stores around the country for use of their name and mascots, but never pays any taxes for those charges.

Why it matters: Due to this setup, billions of dollars in tax revenue are lost every year both in the States where these companies have a real presence and to the federal government. Other States cannot compete with this tax shelter without severely undermining their own collection systems and harming citizens. Many companies have manipulated this methodology to have a zero percent tax rate in other States where they have a physical location.

Of note: Hundreds of thousands of businesses, including 80% of all public corporations, have made Delaware their "home" in order to attain these unwarranted gains. This is despite the fact that a majority of them have absolutely no employees there and count the *Corporation Trust Center*— a small, two-story office building in Wilmington—as their base of operations.

▌ THE PLAN

In order to close the loophole, the President has recommended Congress pass a piece of legislation that covers these three areas:

(1) Should a company larger than a certain size (to avoid impacting small businesses and sole proprietorships) want to have a "location" anywhere, it would need to have a unique, dedicated space that only they use, which must be manned by at least one full-time employee. This would mitigate the current practice used by hundreds of thousands of organizations that simply set up a mail drop in a small building. Even those that choose to remain in Delaware would be required to get a local office space of their own and have at least one employee cover the space.

(2) In the same vein, a company would be required to have a "primary mission" location in the same State that they register their company. For instance, if your company sold widgets, it would need to have some type of facility also in that same State that either manufacturers or sells those widgets, or provides support services (i.e., finance, IT, sales and marketing, etcetera) necessary for the development of those widgets. They could not just incorporate in that State for the benefits while keeping all main functions elsewhere.

(3) Finally, the President wants language to be created that states tangible and intangible assets, royalties, and related charges must all be treated equally under tax law. This would seemingly make it impossible to have a zero-percent tax rate as even the most corporate-friendly States would still want to charge a company located there *something*.

▌ LIKELIHOOD OF ACTION

Yes, but: This is all easier said than done. State and

federal legislatures have tried for decades to close the *Delaware Loophole* to no avail. Many compromise bills have been watered down and thus have limited the intended effect. Further, corporate-hospitable States are reticent to give up what little competitive advantages they have over their neighbors.

Other issues: A few States like Nevada have tried to replicate much of Delaware's scheme in order to lure companies in and encourage them to set up shop there instead, hoping that volume would make up for the difference lost in individual earnings. They might see these proposals as an attack on their nascent strategies.

One more thing: The President asked the single Representative and two Senators from Delaware to "put on your earmuffs for the next few minutes" before launching into the introduction of this concept.

▌ GO BEYOND

- *Biden personally uses tax loophole that Obama administration tried to close*

- *Hilary Clinton and Donald Trump each have a corporate address at this building in Delaware*

- *PA politician who campaigned on closing the "Delaware Loophole" is in hot water for using it*

PRESIDENT WANTS TO DOWNSIZE MILITARY, LEGALIZE DRUGS AND PROSTITUTION

THESE ARE AMONG THE WHITE HOUSE'S PLANS TO BALANCE THE BUDGET AND FIX THE ECONOMY

Piles of United States currency. Photo by **MARKBUCKAWICKI**, *CC0, via Wikimedia Commons.*

February 27th (Portland, OR) – During a rare first-year State of the Union address, the President of the United States proposed a number of new, expanded, and reallocated programs. This included creating considerable controls over medical billing; investing in research that may lead to lowering the death rate related to heart disease; building massive desalination plants and filling the deserts with water; deploying more renewable and nuclear energy capabilities (along with carbon sequestration); constructing an elevator to space; and starting a two-year required national service for 18-year-olds. Of course, all of those high ideals brought up one question...

How are we going to pay for all of this?

▎ CUTTING MILITARY EXPENDITURES

Though the President had already proposed the idea of closing a tax avoidance mechanism known as the "Delaware Loophole", that would hardly put much of a dent on the already multi-trillion-dollar United States budget. Further, the White House itself has now conflated the issue by demanding that Congress pass a balanced budget—that is, one in which expected revenues are to meet or exceed planned expenses without borrowing any money, something that has not been accomplished since the dawn of the 21st century. As such, the President has highlighted one area in which the administration expects there to be cuts. Said the President:

THE ARMED FORCES, SECURITY ORGANIZATIONS, INTELLIGENCE COMMUNITY, AND RELATED SUPPORT COST THIS COUNTRY—IN A TIME OF PEACE, MIND YOU—WELL OVER A TRILLION DOLLARS EVERY YEAR. HOW MUCH OVER A TRILLION? THAT IS NEARLY IMPOSSIBLE TO FIGURE OUT.

In particular, the President highlighted several troubling statistics. First off, no other country on Earth spends as much on their military as the United States. Just comparing armed forces expenditures alone, America clocks in at nearly $800 million. Meanwhile, the runner-up is the U.S.'s perennial global adversary China, which only pays around $250 million. As a matter of fact, the United States outspends the next dozen countries combined—namely, in addition to China: India, Russia, the United Kingdom, Saudi Arabia, France, Germany, Japan, South Korea, Italy, Australia, and Brazil.

Still, some may say that most of these other countries are incomparable to a nation set up like the United States. To this, the President provided the example of the European Union (E.U.) as a whole. With nearly 30 member-states after the recent ascensions of Ukraine and Moldova, the E.U. is relatively the same physical size as the U.S.A., but is more densely populated with around 500 million people compared to 350 million. And despite sharing borders with known aggressor states like Russia and their allies, the E.U. still maintains a military budget under $250 million.

Total expenditures were not the only way to slice the data, though, as the President highlighted. When looking at spending per citizen, the United States is third in the world, below only Israel and the United Arab Emirates. Similarly, America is the second highest payor per soldier with only Libya spending more—despite the fact that India, China, and Russia have far more active members in their armed forces. The President obviously found these figures unimpressive as in a follow-up comment the Commander-in-Chief stated:

 WHAT THIS TELLS ME IS THAT THE UNITED STATES IS NOT SPENDING ITS MONEY WISELY. WE SHOULD BE GETTING MORE

FOR LESS, NOT LESS FOR MORE. THESE NUMBERS ARE CLEAR: WE ARE HIGHLY INEFFICIENT AND NEED TO DO BETTER... MUCH BETTER.

To this end, the President asked—or more accurately demanded—that Congress cut military expenditures by 25% each year over the next three to four years until such a point that the United States became more in-line with its peers. These cuts, the President contended, would more than cover the expenditures of all of the programs the administration has proposed and then some. Neither the non-partisan *Congressional Budget Office* (CBO) nor economic experts have weighed in on whether the President's assumptions are true.

Opponents in Congress and elsewhere have blasted the President. Said one well-known Senator who is considered a potential candidate for the next Presidential election:

 THIS SO-CALLED PRESIDENT STARTED ON DAY ONE BY MAKING THE WORLD LESS SAFE. HAMSTRINGING OUR DEFENSIVE TOOLS AGAINST TERRORISTS, DEPLETING OUR DEPLOYMENTS AROUND THE WORLD, ATTACKING OUR ALLIES IN DANGEROUS ZONES, AND LETTING RUSSIA AND CHINA BE THE WORLD'S LEADERS... JUST ADD SLASHING OUR MILITARY READINESS TO THIS ALREADY BURNING PILE OF GARBAGE.

When asked to respond, the White House Communications Director noted that while the President believes the United

States needs a strong military to be safe and maintain our freedoms, it does not need one with near unlimited funds and no accountability.

▌ VERY NOVEL SOURCES OF REVENUE

Nevertheless, just cutting spending was not the President's only plan. Instead, the administration would like to see the "War on Drugs" ended—which would be a cost savings unto itself—and then, with that, create a new revenue-generating program. As the President explained:

> OF THE TWO MILLION PEOPLE BEHIND BARS IN THE UNITED STATES, 1-IN-5 OF THEM IS THERE FOR SOMETHING RELATED TO DRUGS, MOST LIKELY NONVIOLENT POSSESSION. THIS IS A COMPLETE WASTE. THE MAJORITY OF DRUG USERS ARE PERFECTLY FUNCTIONING PEOPLE AND VALUABLE MEMBERS OF SOCIETY. FOR THE SMALL MINORITY THAT SUFFER FROM ADDICTION, REHABILITATION AND HEALTH SERVICES WOULD BE FAR LESS EXPENSIVE THAN INCARCERATION.

The President then outlined a five-point plan that the administration hopes will be acceptable to all sides:

(1) **Decriminalization** – The President said that possession should not be a criminal offense so as not to fill-up jails and prisons, while at the same time refocusing law enforcement efforts towards those trying to circumvent the yet to be determined management processes;

(2) **Regulation** – The administration believes that not only should all recreational drugs be legal, but that the *Food and Drug Administration* (FDA) ought to be able to maintain quality and safety, just as they do with all other substances that are consumed;

(3) **Taxation** – "We need to get something in return," the President said, in order to afford the expanded role of the FDA, as well as the next two programs;

(4) **Education** – The White House wants the tax dollars generated by drug consumption to be directed towards public outreach and in-school courses on the "honest benefits and dangers of all of these substances" so that people can make their own informed decisions; and

(5) **Rehabilitation** – "And should all else fail," the President noted, "then we will have those tax dollars generated by users to support a safety net for those that do have an addiction or other problem."

Public polling shows that the majority of the country would support these or similar measures—at least for marijuana—with even conservative districts having been much more receptive to such ideas in recent times. Still, it might be a bigger pill to swallow when talking about harder drugs like the opioid fentanyl that have torn communities apart. After being questioned on this after the State of the Union, the President conceded that it might be more palatable to start with "more mainstream drugs" and slowly legalize the rest over time. When further pressed to provide examples of "mainstream" drugs, the President demurred. Based upon historical precedent and current trends, though, aside from marijuana, this could include other psychedelics like LSD and psilocybin (mushrooms). Studies going back to the

2010s that have contrasted the fatality of these and other substances compared to alcohol have found them to be much "safer". Per those examinations, even cocaine had a lower chance of an overdose death than alcohol. Only opiates like heroin fared worse in these investigations.

However, controlled substances were not the extent of the President pushing the boundaries of what many may find permissible. Up next in that bucket was a proposal for the decriminalization of "consensual adult sex work", which most would recognize as "prostitution". The leader of the free world outlined a plan based largely on the rural counties in Nevada where prostitution is already legal. The focus was on the wellbeing of workers, customers, and the community. This included:

- Having designated zoning within a commercial district and not inside or near residential or industrial areas;

- Requiring that all solicitation and transaction activities happen indoors (i.e., no "street workers");

- Using the *Occupational Safety and Health Administration* (OSHA) to confirm safe working conditions, to make sure safe-sex procedures are followed, and to assure testing for sexually transmitted diseases happens on a regular basis;

- Ensure through existing Federal and State agencies that fair wages are received and support the rights of workers to organize; and

- Use freed-up investigative resources to eliminate underage and international trafficking.

These measures, the President contended, would again reduce costs and would instead help replenish the coffers of the government through tax collections. And this would all happen while also decreasing the use of an unregulated and dangerous black market. Here, the President highlighted to a skeptical Congress that since 2020 more than half of Americans have supported decriminalizing sex work, with the averages rising swiftly among younger voters.

Finally, the President expressed a desire to give up something many others who have sat in the Oval Office have enjoyed over the last century:

 AND IF YOU ARE LOOKING FOR EVEN MORE DOLLARS, THEN PLEASE USE THE POWER GRANTED TO THIS CONGRESS BY *ARTICLE 4 § SECTION 3 § CLAUSE 2* OF OUR CONSTITUTION TO "DISPOSE OF... OTHER PROPERTY BELONGING TO THE UNITED STATES" BY SELLING OFF CAMP DAVID. NOTHING IS MORE THE ANTITHESIS OF WHAT IT MEANS TO BE A PUBLIC SERVANT THAN FOR ME, AS THE PRESIDENT, TO HAVE MY OWN PRIVATE 125-ACRE COUNTRY RETREAT. PLEASE, TAKE THIS AWAY FROM ME AND MY SUCCESSORS AND USE THOSE FUNDS ON THE GREAT PEOPLE OF THIS LAND, INSTEAD.

The President did not stop there and asked Congress to review all properties owned by the Federal Government that could be sold off at a profit, excluding lands being protected for environmental, quality of life, security, and indigenous uses. Further, the President wanted Congress to entertain the idea of accepting sponsorship for buildings and structures that the government does own—such as is done with stadium naming rights—which would provide a desperately needed novel revenue stream.

▍SEVEN MONTHS TO FIGURE IT OUT

After all of this, the President wrapped up the administration's desires and requirements for the budget and the economy—as well as the State of the Union in general—with an ominous forewarning. It was at this point that the President indicated that the federal budget, in its entirety, must be passed by the end of the fiscal year, which is on September 30th. For decades, Congress has been running in a piecemeal fashion by passing various parts of the budget for differing lengths of time, anywhere from a few days to several years. This disjointed methodology has resulted in several limited partial-government shutdowns when they have not been passed and signed-off on in time.

Each of these acts have become known as "continuing resolutions" and the President has indicated the administration's support for them would remain, but only on a very limited basis. Said the President:

DESPITE EVERYTHING YOU HAVE HEARD ME SAY, I WILL SUPPORT AND SIGN-OFF ON ANY CONTINUING RESOLUTION THIS CONGRESS GIVES ME. HOWEVER, I WILL IMMEDIATELY VETO ANY OF THESE FUNDING MECHANISMS THAT EXTENDS BEYOND SEPTEMBER 30TH. FOR FUNDING ANY PART OF

THE GOVERNMENT AFTER SEPTEMBER 30TH, YOU MUST GIVE ME A COMPLETE AND CLEAN BUDGET THAT COVERS THE ENTIRE FEDERAL GOVERNMENT AND SPANS THE WHOLE FISCAL YEAR.

The President continued by saying that any budget that did not cut military spending by 25% while also reappropriating at least some of those funds towards any of the programs and ideas the President had laid out will be met with an automatic veto. The President let Congress know that the only way they could escape the chief executive's veto would be to garner enough votes to overturn it.

And that is the real rub. With Congress so evenly split between Democrats and Republicans (and the independents that caucus with them) and the President not aligned with either, no one appears poised to compromise. Political experts fear that Democrats and Republicans will push their own preferred policies without taking the President or the other Political Party into account. If that is the situation, Congress will lack the $\frac{2}{3}$rds majority necessary to override the President's veto, even if they manage to pass a budget or continuing resolution on mostly Party lines through a reconciliation process.

That said, even getting to that point is a tall order since there are many renegades even within the Republican and Democratic Parties. In the times when either of the dominant Parties had complete control over Congress and the White House, they still struggled to pass any major legislation due to these mavericks. Many of them could potentially be placated with a bone thrown to their district that they can take credit for, but sometimes in small groups they are impossible to appease.

Only time will tell if the President will be successful or if Congress will find its own path. Nonetheless, the White House has committed to working with Congress, starting immediately, to resolve their differences and come up with a budget that can be supported by most. After all, they have over seven months to arrive at a reasonable conclusion, otherwise the entire Federal Government will completely shut down.

And that does not benefit anyone, least of all the politicians that would potentially cause it.

[T]HINK OF THE SOLUTION, NOT THE PROBLEM. IF YOUR MIND WAS FILLED ONLY WITH THOUGHTS OF WHY YOU WERE GOING TO LOSE, THEN YOU COULDN'T THINK OF HOW TO WIN.

FROM *BLOOD OF THE FOLD* BY TERRY GOODKIND

OVER THERE?

FOR WOMEN'S HISTORY MONTH, PRESIDENT BLASTS THE REST OF THE WORLD

READ THE FULL SPEECH BEFORE THE SONOMA COUNTY COMMISSION ON THE STATUS OF WOMEN

A view overlooking the older and newer neighborhoods of Jerusalem, with the Dome of the Rock and the Western Wall in the middle. Photo by J.P. Prag on January 17, 2007.

March 11th (Santa Rosa, CA) – March is **Women's History Month**, which started right here in Santa Rosa as just a single week in 1978. By 1980, the week became recognized at the federal level before expanding to the whole month in 1987. It was a great surprise and honor, then, that the recently installed President of the United States requested to give a speech before the **Commission on the Status of Women**—which founded and administered the original celebratory week—to commemorate this year's observances.

While the Commission has certainly expressed acknowledgement of topics not directly related to the "status of women"—notably that the Commission itself functions on the "ancestral lands of the Pomo, Wappo, and Coast Miwok" peoples—many in the audience were surprised how far off-topic the President took these prepared remarks. Instead of being about women's history and the ongoing fight for equality, the President gave a sprawling speech covering a wide array of oppressive elements around the entire globe.

▌BELOW IS A TRANSCRIPT OF THE PRESIDENT'S SPEECH IN ITS ENTIRETY

Thank you all for having me here today. It is my extreme pleasure and privilege to be able to stand before the very people who helped raise the bar on recognizing the contributions of women throughout the history of our nation. Sadly, the struggle for equality among the sexes is an ongoing battle, one that I know everyone here—myself included—will never retreat from.

But with that said, I believe it is important to also recognize the continual oppression happening to marginalized communities elsewhere in the world. As I have made very clear since Inauguration Day, we need to stand up to those who do not share our values, damn the consequences. For if we are not living up to the ideals we claim to have, then we do not deserve to call ourselves the land of the free!

So please indulge me as I highlight a few examples of these less fortunate individuals who need our attention, sympathy, and support as they are trapped in uncaring lands, under indifferent and sometimes brutal regimes.

First off, I want to talk about a country in the Middle East that has created an entirely different legal system that suppresses the rights of the native Islamic Arabs while the European immigrants who have only recently arrived have near carte blanche freedom to do whatever they want. Should an indigenous person commit the same acts as these Anglo invaders, they will find themselves detained, tortured, mutilated, and barely given a show trial, if they are lucky.

Of course, I am talking about the **United Arab Emirates**.

Similarly, there are places on this planet that are beneath the thumb of colonial invaders. The aboriginals of these lands live under intolerable conditions, even lacking the freedom of movement to see their own compatriots right next door. For generations now, whole families have been torn asunder while the world turns a blind eye for political expedience.

Of course, I'm talking about Northern Cyprus by **Türkiye**, *Western Sahara by* **Morocco**, *and Kabylia by* **Algeria**. *And do I even need to bring up* **Russia** *and* **China**?

Not to be forgotten, there are places where the occupiers do not even originate from the same continent, yet still hold on to the land despite the fact that the ethnic natives just want to create and maintain a stable, peaceful nation of their own—the right of any people.

Of course, I am talking about **Spain** *with their ill-gotten holdings along the northern African coast including Ceuta, Melilla, and the Plazas de Soberanía.*

Keeping some particular population from troubling you can

become the preoccupation of an entire nation, even after they have supposedly left that area. For instance, there is a country that used to occupy a small strip of land on the Mediterranean Coast. Yet even while claiming to no longer having anything to do with that densely populated place after withdrawing, they still maintain a level of domination through economic measures. Most notably in recent times, they have set up a blockade that unilaterally punishes the populous en masse for the actions of the government in charge.

Of course, I am talking about **Egypt**, which used to occupy, control, and oversee the Gaza Strip under military rule from 1949 to 1967. Today, they deploy a land, sea, and air embargo because it suits their own personal interests.

Still, there are even worse places. There is a country which actively engages in apartheid, amazingly somehow happening in our time. When the modern version of this country formed in the mid-20th century, it was with the hope that it would provide protections for its unique tribal peoples, ones who had greatly suffered at the hands of Europeans. However, that protectionism turned into xenophobia, which in turn became hysteria, to which finally became institutional racism, misogamy, and bigotry. Now, only one type of the "chosen" with one specific religion have any semblance of freedom there, and, as far as the law is concerned, the others do not even exist.

Of course, I am talking about **Saudi Arabia**, which I am sure the attendees here will recognize for the less-than-human way they treat all women. And it cannot be highlighted enough how they treat non-Muslims, and even different sects within Islam.

As hard as it is to believe, there are places in the world where the treatment of people is even more severe. For instance, a certain group of people have been kept in refugee camps for several generations now; having no home, no country, nor any way to leave. Their so-called "hosts" forcefully refuse to let them be anything more than political pawns to be flaunted when convenient, such as when the scaremongering overseers want to get people in a tizzy or spread panic among their own citizens.

*Of course, I am talking about **Lebanon**, **Syria**, and **Jordan** that have all blatantly rejected allowing Palestinians to leave the open-air detention centers where they have been involuntary trapped. This state of affairs is still ongoing even though almost everyone in these camps are descendants of someone who fled their home generations ago. Those who originally left are mostly dead, yet their progenies are still paying that penance.*

Sometimes, though, the oppressors are not satisfied with merely having human beings living in squalor with no hope, but instead want those same people to suffer even more. In a country like this, in order to maintain their power, violence is the government's preferred response. Where poor farmers and fisherman try to just scrape by, this country responds with live fire and disproportionate and indiscriminate bombings. This is especially true in any area that the government claims as "disputed", even though the holdings obviously have nothing to do with the conquerors and historically have belonged to another group. And it is fair to note that they only have this supremacy because of how the colonial British withdrew from the area and partitioned the lands to give much of it away to a specific ethno-religious group, no matter where they happened to really originate from.

Of course, I am talking about **Pakistan**, a vast military power that will use any means necessary to maintain their iron grip over places like Kashmir.

All of these previously mentioned countries are not the only ones that tell individuals how to live their lives. There are also governments—nations that claim to be democracies with a steep tradition in social welfare—that have the audacity to tell people, especially women, what they can and cannot wear. Even more so, they racially profile people of Middle Eastern and East Asian descent with these laws, not even hiding their intentions.

Of course, I am talking about **France** and **Switzerland**, two countries that have banned head and face coverings in public in a blatant attempt to oppress the expression of traditional Islamic identity and to tell women what they can and cannot do with their own bodies.

Sadly, just taking control of people's physical and personal lives is not enough for some countries. There is a nation that is actively working towards ethnically "cleansing" their cities of those they find undesirable, despite the fact that the folks that they are trying to purge have been there for time immemorial. This government wants only one type of populace with one set of beliefs to inhabit their cities in order to create "facts on the ground", no matter how contrary to history and human rights that may be.

Of course, I am talking about **Ethiopia**, as they are fervently transferring ethnic Tigrayans out of their homes so that only the "true" Ethiopians remain in the areas under the government's complete control.

Transferring populations and replacing them with your own

is against international law, and some would say rises to the level of genocide. However, in this case, those who have been taken from their homes are thankfully still alive. In one country I am thinking about, the "undesirables" do not even have that chance. The government comes in, razes their homes for made up offenses, and—if I can be blunt—straight up murders them in order to seize their lands and make sure they can never come back.

*Of course, I am talking about the ethnic cleansing of the Rohingya at the hands of **Myanmar**. And I would be remiss not to note that Myanmar partook in these activities both as a military dictatorship and as an elected democracy— the latter under the auspices of the head of the government who won a Nobel Peace Prize for "her non-violent struggle for democracy and human rights."*

With so much violence, people have had to flee as refugees to other nations. But there is one country that—even though their modern nation was basically founded by refugees—refuses to take almost anyone in, with one exception: if the immigrants are of a preferred religion. And let me be very clear; their laws specifically make it so that Muslims are persona non grata while people from one specific sect are granted expedited settlement and automatic citizenship.

*Of course, I am talking about **India**, which in the 2020s passed a series of measures to give Hindu migrants a preferred status while explicitly attempting to keep those who practice other religions, most especially Islam, out of the country.*

This brings up the concept of "jus sanguinis", which translates as the "right of blood"; or "leges sanguinis", which loosely means "birthright by ethnicity". In either case, these are ethnic/race-based beliefs that certain people "belong" to a physical country, no matter how removed and disconnected those people may be from that land. These philosophies allow a specific nation to welcome the demographic they want, grant them immediate residency and even citizenship, and make sure the country maintains a specific character. In the meantime, the "others" are excluded, oftentimes with no way to ever attain what those with the right blood can access with almost zero effort.

*Of course, I am talking about countries like **Armenia**, **Rwanda**, and **South Korea**, among many others. The idea of a pluralistic society like we have in the United States is lost on these nations.*

Unfortunately, what seems to be forgotten in all of this is that it is not about land, it is about people, all people, all of humanity. In the late 1940s, a group of people that had already suffered tremendously suddenly found themselves thrust from their homes. Over 800,000 people were abruptly made stateless refugees because of a reaction to what was happening hundreds, even thousands of miles away. They were found guilty by association based on their ethno-religious identity. The governments and even the common folks stole their homes, their possessions, their businesses, and—most of all—their dignity. And to this day, neither they nor their descendants have received so much as an apology, nonetheless reparations.

*Of course, I am talking about the **United Nations** which failed in its very infancy by not preventing the expulsion of more than 800,000 Jewish people from majority Arab, Persian, and Islamic countries like **Iraq**, **Iran**, **Yemen**, **Libya**, **Tunisia**, and plenty more. Sadly, the bulk of them died* *before ever getting to see their homelands one last time.*

But what we are really talking about here is freedom, and freedom comes from self-determination. Yet many govern-ments claim they are representative democracies, trying to whitewash over their crimes and oppressive regimes. An administration like this maintains their authority by claim-ing that they are the only spokesperson for their ethno-religious group. Anyone who disagrees with them is called a "racist". Further, they have the "right" to take any and all action against the "others"—as well as those within their own nebulous borders—to protect themselves and their land.

*Of course, I am talking about **Palestine** which has not had an election in decades! During that last campaign, the rul-ing PLO actually lost to the terrorist organization Hamas, which lead to a mini-civil war that split the Palestinians up between those who now live in Gaza and those in Judea and Samaria. When Mahmoud Abbas was selected as Pres-ident in 2005, it was for a five-year term. Yet there have been no elections and the people have not had an oppor-tunity to vote since then, and he stayed on as President until his death much, much later. Then there was another mini-civil war followed by a unification deal to place one of his chosen successors onto the seat of power with a plan for an election within a year; an election that to this day has still not happened.*

A freedom that many people aspire for is the ability to ex-press their own faith. Being a staunch supporter of the separation of Church and state, it disgusts me that there is a country out there that uses their police force to only allow those who practice one religion unfettered access to pray at a very holy site. As a matter of fact, entrance to other adherents is severely restricted to the point where there are times that the government flatly denies access for these pious people to even visit in a non-religious capacity, a decision based solely upon the faith they were born into.

Of course, I am talking about **Israel** which does not allow Jews to pray at the Temple Mount, also known as al-Ḥaram al-Sharīf in Muslim tradition. In order to appease the Palestinians, the Jordanians, and the Islamic world in general, Israel has restricted access so that Jewish people cannot express their devotion in a way they best see fit for themselves. And to be fair, it is not just Jews that are denied freedom to express their beliefs, but so, too, are Christians and those who adhere to any other non-Muslim belief. Yes, the state itself is sponsoring Islam as the only acceptable religion in an area, and this does not sit well with me at all.

And finally, let me tell you about one last country. This place treats any non-majority person as a second-class citizen; not by law, but by action. Further, this nation actually disproportionality imprisons minorities; though, in truth, based on its total population, it imprisons the highest percentage of its population compared to anywhere else in the world.

While this is going on at home, it possesses far-flung, non-contiguous territories where its own laws do not apply. And how it gained control over those lands was through vast military actions that displaced and killed scores of civilians. Yet direct military action is not the only tool this country uses, as they have engaged in targeted assassinations without any trial or recourse. Meanwhile, they close their borders to peaceful economic migrants, treating them the same as enemy combatants.

However, even after so many years of being a nation, they still do not have a clear and defined border with their northern neighbor, despite ages of never-ending negotiations that have sometimes come to blows. This country even challenged their own agreement of the land boundary applying to the sea and demanded far more, using their superior military might to avoid ever having to resolve the issue.

*This country that I speak of is the **United States America**. Women, people of color, immigrants, non-native English speakers—basically anyone who is not a white heterosexual cisgender male—has a much more difficult time here. Yes, the law claims to be equal for all people, but the realities of the application of law and the implementation among its institutions is a different story entirely. And when those lacking power and representation step out of line, or appear to step out of line, then they are far more likely to be punished by the law and have massively more severe penalties for similar offenses. There is no quarter, forgiveness, understanding, or true rehabilitation for the over two million people who sit behind bars.*

I have spoken in depth about what has happened at Guantanamo Bay and how I have tried to shut it down, but there are more places like this all over the world. Black sites are a real thing, places where American laws and values do not exist, where the ends justify the means. Even I, the President of the United States, cannot know every mission out there, every actionable plan, and I cannot guarantee that our intelligence services are not engaging in activities like assassinations and regime changes even as we speak, despite my directives.

Meanwhile, people are just trying to get into this country, not to take it over, but to make a living for their family. Our government lacks any sympathy, even though we are completely dependent upon migrant labor to make our own economy work. This was made painfully clear to everyone during the COVID-19 pandemic and its aftermath, yet it still never spurred Congress to action.

Amazingly, though, it is not just our southern neighbor we cannot seem to make peace with. Since the late 1800s we have been fighting with Canada over a little strip of land near Alaska called "Dixon Entrance", one of four border disputes that we have not been able to resolve. Canada could not be a better neighbor, but we use our might to get the resources we want, even when dealing with a good friend. If this is how we treat our closest allies, can you not then see how these actions damage our relationships with the rest of the world?

So, when I think of us, here in the United States of America, I have only one thought:

Before we cast disparaging remarks directed at others, we have to look at ourselves in the mirror. We must first answer for our own shortcomings prior to telling the rest of the world how they should live and act. The best way to change the world is to change ourselves first. And once we do that, we can lead by example instead of by word alone.

To the women in this room, here to commemorate a month dedicated to you, you do deserve much more than this country has given you. But I would like you to be able to also reflect on how much progress you have made, especially in comparison to the troubles seen in the rest of the world. Nothing was handed to you; you had to fight for everything. So please, lend your strength to those who need it, and remember that freedom and opportunity are never assured, only seized from those who would try to withhold them from you.

PRESIDENT DECREES AMERICA IS THE MOST COMMUNIST NATION ON EARTH

GET READY TO DROP THE BLUE AND WHITE AND HAVE A WHOLE LOT MORE RED IN THAT FLAG

A hammer and sickle are laid out over red drapery in this photo by SA-RANG, Public Domain, via Wikimedia Commons.

April 11th (Alabaster, AL) – This past Friday, the President of the United States sat down with the largest socialist periodical in America—one that we will refrain from naming in these prestigious pages in order not to lend them any credence and legitimacy. As established during the third day of this administration, the President brought an end to the routine of daily press briefings and regular access to the White House and replaced them with a free-for-all end-of-week one-on-one bonanza. While the leader of the free world was more than happy to spend time with socialists, I would be remiss if I did not point out that the President has still not sat down with yours truly.

Is the President afraid of what a real reporter would ask? Or is the administration showing their true colors by only letting those with certain viewpoints through the gatekeepers? They claim the process is randomized, but it is quite clear who they are excluding.

You may be saying to yourself, "Wait a minute, Friday was a few days ago. Why did it take so long to bring this to our attention?" Well, intrepid reader, the White House does not announce who is selected for their privileged access and leaves it up to each outlet whether they want anyone to know ahead of time or not. Up until this point, everyone—even the social media stars—at least had the decency to put out their reports by Friday evening or Saturday morning at the latest. But not this crew! Apparently, this socialist bulletin was so completely disorganized and unprepared that they could not get anything out the door on time. Who would have guessed that a bunch of lazy socialists (redundant?) couldn't even be bothered to do what they claim are their jobs?

And what a job they did! In a rambling, nonsensical, poorly edited (spell checker is automatic, people!), and downright painful to read diatribe, the so-called interviewer for this article tried to lead the President into admitting to being a straight-up communist. Surely the President of the United States was too smart to be manipulated into stating such foolishness by a highly functioning moron, right?

Well, my friends, you are in for a surprise (or not)! Also, you can thank me now for wading through this dreck so you didn't have to. Per usual, from the sweat of my brow, here is the good stuff...

IT'S WORD SALAD DAY WITH YOUR SUBSTITUTE TEACHER: THE PRESIDENT OF THE UNITED STATES

Let's start off with the utterances right from the President's own mouth-hole:

> **WHAT DO I THINK? I BELIEVE THE UNITED STATES OF AMERICA IS THE MOST COMMUNIST NATION IN THE WORLD.**

Well, there you have it, everyone! What more needs to be said?

Apparently, a lot, because the President went on a rant for quite a while after this. You see, the President only believes in the "academic definition of communism" that the elite take straight from Karl Marx's *The Communist Manifesto*. As the President explained it, in that book Marx put forth a theory that there is a natural evolution of ownership over the "means of production." This started with the producers being slaves and the owners being city-states to the producers being serfs and the owners being landowners within larger states. In modern capitalism, that has turned into the employee and corporate management relationship. Thus, by Marx's and the President's estimation, the "natural evolution" would be reached when the producers and the owners were the same people.

Except, of course, this never happened. Instead, we got the USSR, China, Cuba, and North Korea. The President did have a response for this, though:

THOSE COUNTRIES ARE "LENINIST", NOT "COMMUNIST". AS I SAID BEFORE, COMMUNISM MEANS THE WORKERS OWN THE MEANS OF PRODUCTION. LENINISM MEANS THE GOVERNMENT IS SACROSANCT AND THE PEOPLE ARE SUBSERVIENT TO IT, BUT IN TURN THE GOVERNMENT PROVIDES EVERYTHING FOR THEM. COMMUNISM HAS NOTHING TO WITH ANY FORM OF GOVERNMENT, CONTRARY TO WHAT FORMED UNDER LENIN, MAO, AND THEIR CONTEMPORARIES.

The millions of people who died under those systems would disagree, dear President, as would Karl Marx himself. The original title of Marx's work was *The Manifesto of the Communist Party*. When someone entitles their handiwork with the literal name of a Political Party, it certainly sounds like government planning to me. But perhaps the President believes that you and I are too proletarian to understand?

Still, the lesson the President was trying to teach us all was not over yet. To hammer and sickle home any doubt on the definition of words, the President clarified:

 I WANT TO DRAW A LINE-IN-THE-SAND BE-TWEEN "COMMUNISM" AND "SOCIALISM". SOCIALISM IS WHERE THE GOVERNMENT PROVIDES SERVICES TO THE PEOPLE. NOW WE COULD GO BIG AND HIGHLIGHT HOW PROGRAMS LIKE SOCIAL SECURITY, MEDI-CARE, AND MEDICAID ARE OBVIOUS ONES THAT WE CAN POINT TO AS BEING SOCIAL-ISM HERE IN THE UNITED STATES. HOWEVER, I WOULD CONTEND THAT EVEN BUILDING ROADS IS SOCIALISM. AS I SAID, "SOCIALISM" IS ANYTHING THE GOVERN-MENT PROVIDES FOR THE PEOPLE.

That is certainly an... interesting... interpretation of social-ism and a genuine attempt to twist it into the President's worldview. But it should be pointed out that there is as massive of a difference between building roads and Social Security as there is between the latter and Venezuela.

Here, it would appear that the President was conflating the administration's own choice of classifications by intermin-gling "socialism" and "communism", but the president did expound upon this:

 YOU ARE PROBABLY ASKING YOURSELF, THEN, WHAT MAKES THE UNITED STATES SO COMMUNIST IF THE SOCIAL WELFARE PRO-GRAMS WE HAVE IMPLEMENTED DON'T COUNT? SIMPLY PUT, IF YOU LOOK AT THE

HOW MUCH EMPLOYEE OWNERSHIP THERE IS THROUGH STOCK OPTION PLANS, STOCK PURCHASE PLANS, EQUITY GRANTS, OWNERSHIP TRUSTS, AND WORKER COOPERATIVES—NO OTHER COUNTRY IN THE WORLD COMES EVEN CLOSE TO THE PERCENTAGE OF WORKERS THAT OWN AT LEAST A SMALL PIECE OF THEIR OWN CURRENT OR FORMER EMPLOYERS.

Certainly, that is a unique stretch of what having proprietorship over the "means of production" signifies. Listen, the President is not wrong that workers can partake in many different plans that get them ownership stakes or stock in their companies. Still, aside from Co-Ops, none would really jive with this argument. Besides, doesn't this just prove how well capitalism works and that it is the superior system?

Sorry Comrade President, your Math and English lessons are just not lining up.

PEACE IN OUR LIFETIME? PRESIDENT TACKLES ISRAELI-PALESTINIAN CONFLICT

WITH FLATTERY, PERSUASION, AND FINALLY OUTRIGHT THREATS, AN UNUSUAL PEACE PROCESS HAS BEEN KICKED OFF IN THE MIDDLE EAST

A sign on the edge of a cliff in southern Israel reads in Hebrew and English "Caution! Abyss Ahead". Photo by J.P. Prag on January 18, 2007.

April 29th (Jerusalem, Israel) – Reporters from around the world had been sequestered into a separate room. There was a palpable tension among everyone there as we awaited any news, anything at all, even the smallest detail. Nothing leaked out from behind those closed doors, temptingly placed just a few meters away across the hall from us. Heavily armed security guards made sure we would not give into our yearnings and would instead maintain a respectful distance. Expressing their agitation, one among our group likened it to being in a waiting room at a hospital, hoping to hear an update about their loved one who was undergoing surgery.

Yet when the doors swung open less than an hour later and the President of the United States stepped through, we were quite surprised. Despite wanting to learn whatever we could from the proceedings, no one truly expected to get anything more than a brief at the end of the day, at the earliest. With a grim face, the President approached the podium and said:

 EVERYONE... WE HAVE AN AGREEMENT. FOR THE FIRST TIME IN HISTORY, THERE IS HOPE THAT WE CAN ACHIEVE PEACE IN THE MIDDLE EAST!

The President then gave a smirk as every reporter sat there completely dumbstruck. And then there was an explosion of sound as a cacophony of journalists launched into a slew of pent-up questions.

HOW WE GOT HERE

Shortly after Inauguration Day, the American President reached out to many world leaders to assure them that the United States was still a partner in maintaining peace and order, despite the administration's actions related to pulling troops out of the international arena and instigating the downfall of the United Nations. This included calls to the Prime Minister of Israel and the President of the Palestinian

Authority, but ostensibly something was left out of the White House's readouts of those conversations.

Sources close to the President later revealed that the American President asked each government head about holding a summit between the three leaders with no specific expectations. Both rulers were keen to meet with the new President, but not while the other one was present. Over the ensuing weeks, the President began to raise the pressure on each one individually, finally resulting in outright threats. For the Israeli side, the President said that the White House would acknowledge Israeli's nuclear program, which in turn would trigger a law (**22 U.S. Code § 2799aa**) that would require the United States to immediately cut off all aid to the country. For reference, the noted law states in part:

 ...[N]O FUNDS... MAY BE USED FOR THE PURPOSE OF PROVIDING ECONOMIC ASSISTANCE... PROVIDING MILITARY ASSISTANCE... OR MAKING GUARANTEES, TO ANY COUNTRY... [THAT] DELIVERS NUCLEAR ENRICHMENT EQUIPMENT, MATERIALS, OR TECHNOLOGY TO ANY OTHER COUNTRY... OR RECEIVES SUCH EQUIPMENT, MATERIALS, OR TECHNOLOGY FROM ANY OTHER COUNTRY ON OR AFTER AUGUST 4, 1977...

While Israel's nuclear capabilities are considered the world's worst kept secret, every successive U.S. regime has not acknowledged it for this very reason, as well as to create an ambiguity around the situation in order not to trigger a nuclear arms race in the Middle East. Of course, the success of this policy is questionable, at best, considering all that has happened since with Iran.

Meanwhile, it has been reported that the President took a similar tactic with the Palestinian Authority. In this case, the President threatened to not only cut off all aid and funding, but to add the entire populous to the terrorist organization list, most especially their leaders, and freeze all of their assets everywhere in the world. Even this intimidation did not seem to be enough as just a few weeks ago the President alluded to the Palestinian leader being an un-elected autocrat during a speech supposedly for *Women's History Month* in Santa Rosa, CA. Many had puzzled over the content of that oration, but apparently it may have been a subtle warning to the Palestinians in order to get them to agree to this summit. Perhaps making references in public was enough to motivate the Palestinian faction into action in fear of what else may be overtly shared if they kept their intransigent stance.

All we know for sure is that just a few short days ago, the meeting between all the parties was officially announced, with more details to follow. However, nothing was announced ahead of time aside from an invitation to the media to attend the summit at an undisclosed location.

▌ THE FIRST AGREEMENT

Even prior to this announcement, not much was known about what the American President's intentions were in relation to the Israeli-Palestinian conflict. As the hour got closer, the only detail that was revealed was that the White House wanted to limit who was going to be in the room to as few people as possible. From the American side, only the President, the ambassador to Israel, the chief of the Palestinian Affairs Unit, a representative from the Office of Security Negotiations and Agreements, and a military technician—for reasons that will be made clear later—made the trip. The Israelis and Palestinians decided to bring a mix of ministers, lead negotiators, and some military personnel, but still each abided by a previously unreported ten-person limit per side. As such, only 25 people in total were in the room as talks began.

After the President came out and announced the aforementioned surprising breakthrough and managed to quiet down the crowd, the military technician then rolled out a monitor. Turing it on, a map that included Israel, Gaza, the West Bank, and other disputed areas was visible. Most of the map was uncolored except for two specific blobs. On the west side, a blue blob was visible within the municipal borders of Tel Aviv. Towards the center, there was a similar green mark filling in Ramallah. The President then explained what we were looking at:

 WHAT YOU ARE SEEING HERE IS THE FIRST AGREEMENT BETWEEN ISRAEL AND THE PALESTINIAN AUTHORITY. EVERY PRIOR PEACE PROCESS HAS ATTEMPTED TO ANSWER ALL QUESTIONS IN ONE GO AND FAILED WHEN THEY COULD NOT. SO, WE ARE GOING TO TAKE A DIFFERENT APPROACH. INSTEAD OF RESOLVING ALL THE ISSUES AT ONCE, WE ARE GOING TO AIM FOR "PETITE CONSENSUSES", DONE ONE SMALL BIT AT A TIME. AND SHOULD NEGOTIATIONS FAIL AT ANY POINT OR WE NEED A LONG

BREAK FOR WHATEVER REASON, THE NEXT
STARTING POINT WILL BE WHERE WE LEFT
OFF. WE WILL NEVER AGAIN BEGIN FROM
ZERO.

The President then expounded upon what had happened in
the room. Apparently, the representatives from the Palestinian Authority had agreed that in any ultimate settlement
Tel Aviv would be in Israel and that they had no claim on
the city. In the same vein, the representatives from Israel
had acquiesced that Ramallah would be in a future independent Palestinian state. Because of this, the President
claimed, they could now build outwards from those starting
points with the parties approving what would be in any final-decision agreement.

And this is where the President made a really astonishing
announcement about the forthcoming sessions. The board
we were looking at would be a live connection to the negotiating room, and as each agreement was made the
monitor in the media room would update instantly. We
could literally watch live as accords were made, making
sure nothing could be hidden. We later learned that the
screen in the negotiating room was a touchscreen with the
capability to cut the region up into parcels as small as a
house.

▌ BEHIND THE SCENES METHODOLOGY

While we in the press room were certainly flummoxed,
those in the negotiating room were also taken completely
unawares. According to one source who was in the room
but wishes to remain anonymous, not one single person
besides the President appeared to know any of this was

coming. The President seemingly hoodwinked them all and then backed everyone into a corner by announcing the terms without even a discussion about the administration's intentions. However, they had little recourse as the President's initial threats used to get all of the parties to the table were still in effect and were being capriciously enforced.

According to the source, this happened right away. After laying out the plan that would be later explained to the press, the President dove right in and asked the Israeli Prime Minister about the country's position on Ramallah. At first, the Prime Minister was reluctant to give any answer, but after a short while conceded that Ramallah—within its current municipal boundaries—would be part of a future Palestinian state without objection. With this, the President had the military technician in the room make the appropriate update on the interactive map.

The same did not exactly happen with the representatives from the Palestinian Authority. Despite the early contrition from Israel, the Palestinians did not appear to want to participate in the process as they considered it a farce. At first, the American President attempted to gently cajole them and asked them to explain any claim they may have over Tel Aviv. When none were forthcoming, the President eventually lost patience. The source then played a recording of the American President for this reporter (warning: strong language ahead):

 JUST STOP THIS BULLSHIT! THERE IS NO FUTURE WORLD IN WHICH TEL AVIV IS IN PALESTINE, UNLESS YOU ARE PLANNING A MASS GENOCIDE. IS THAT YOUR

INTENTION? DO YOU WANT TO ANNOUNCE TO THE WORLD YOU SUPPORT A HOLOCAUST OF THE JEWISH PEOPLE?

The Palestinian President insisted that he was being maligned, misquoted, and misunderstood, and that neither he nor anyone in the Palestinian Authority would suggest such a thing. The American President was silent for a long moment, turning away from everyone else. Finally, spinning around, the President declared:

FINE, YOU KNOW WHAT, THEN HERE'S THE DEAL: IF YOU ARE GOING TO JUST KEEP FIGHTING ME ON THIS PROCESS, I'M GOING TO WALK OUT TO THAT ROOM OF REPORTERS AND TELL THEM THAT THE ISRAELIS WERE WILLING TO MAKE MASSIVE CONCESSIONS FOR PEACE AND YOUR RESPONSE WAS YOU WERE GOING TO RAZE TEL AVIV AND COMMIT AN EXTERMINATION OF THE JEWISH PEOPLE. I WILL TELL THEM THAT THERE IS NO HOPE FOR PEACE BECAUSE THE PALESTINIANS WANT NOTHING BUT WAR, AND THAT THE UNITED STATES AND THE WORLD ARE DONE WITH SUPPORTING THEIR USELESS PHONY CAUSE. AND THEN I'M GOING TO DECLARE EVERY SINGLE PALESTINIAN GROUP, BUSINESS, AND PERSON UNDER YOUR REGIME A TERRORIST. FINALLY, I WILL COMPLETELY DESTROY WHAT LITTLE IS LEFT OF YOUR ECONOMY AND DECLARE

UNCONDITIONAL MILITARY SUPPORT FOR
ISRAEL, STARTING BY TAKING ALL OF THE
FUNDING THAT WAS GOING TO YOU AND
GIVING IT TO THEM.

At first, the Palestinian contingent balked at this outright extortion. After much haranguing, the Palestinian President said he was insulted by such remarks, but did not believe this tale, saying he was calling the Americans' bluff. The American President then pulled a sheaf of papers out of a bag and showed it to everyone in the room. The offered document was an Executive Order that the administration had already written up with the details exactly as the President had described them. All it required was the Commander-in-Chief's signature to immediately take effect. There was some wavering, but it was not until the American President was halfway out the door that the Palestinians called the President back and finally, reluctantly agreed that Tel Aviv was part of Israel and would remain so in any concluding treaty. It was at this point that the President reportedly cheered with what was described as "snide" delight, updated the map, and immediately walked out the door to tell us in the press room what had transpired.

FUTURE NEGOTIATIONS

What was left unsaid was the President must have had a similar Executive Order ready for the Israelis if they did not play ball. While it did not come to that, the administration was surely prepared for such a possibility.

Now the question seems to be: what happens next? The American President said that now that the process had been laid out and agreed upon, it did not require the Commander-in-Chief's personal attention every single day. Instead, the rest of the team would continue on in the White House's stead with a focus on agreements and putting disputes "in the parking lot" until they could be explored later on. Said the leader of the free world:

I DON'T EXPECT THIS TO BE EASY, AND THERE ARE A LOT OF QUESTIONS MORE DIFFICULT THAN LAND-CONTROL THAT WE HAVE TO ANSWER. THERE ARE THINGS LIKE THE "RIGHT OF RETURN", REPARATIONS, CITIZENSHIP, FREE MOVEMENT, SECURITY, AND MORE. I'LL STEP IN WHEN I NEED TO, BUT I BELIEVE IT IS MOST IMPORTANT FOR THE PARTIES TO MAKE THESE DECISIONS AMONG THEMSELVES WITH US JUST ACTING AS MEDIATORS... AND PRODDING THEM A LITTLE BIT WHEN NEED BE.

Time will tell if this approach is any better than all the other ones that have fallen apart before any progress was made, but it is clear that this is a novel approach that may yet make that elusive breakthrough towards actual peace.

THE SECRET WARS THE PRESIDENT DOES NOT WANT YOU TO KNOW ABOUT

COULD THE UNITED STATES BE BEHIND UPRISINGS AROUND THE WORLD, ALL WHILE CLAIMING TO BE THE HARBINGERS OF PEACE?

*On July 8, 2017, Pakistan attacked an Indian Army post in retaliation for the latter allegedly firing into disputed Kashmir. Photo by **INTER SERVICES PUBLIC RELATIONS DIRECTORATE (PAKISTAN) WEB SITE**, [1], Attribution, via Wikimedia Commons.*

May 14th (Detroit, MI) – Is the President of the United States a person of peace, or a purveyor of war? As details leak out from behind the scenes of the White House, the question is becoming more and more difficult to answer.

On the one hand is Inauguration Day, when the President unilaterally pared down the country's nuclear arsenal, closed Guantanamo Bay, and withdrew troops from around the world. On the other hand, during that same flurry of Executive Orders, the President demolished the top peace-keeping force in the world in the United Nations and intentionally antagonized other countries by implementing a new labeling system for them, judging where they fell on a loosely defined scale.

Just a few weeks ago, the President initiated a reconciliation process between Israel and Palestine, which has been a nearly hopeless endeavor for decades. Yet in order to get that kick-started, the President reportedly had to threaten both parties with potential annihilation. When asked about this tactic upon returning stateside, the President gave a perplexing answer:

YOU KNOW, IN MANY WAYS, MY MIND IS NOT FOCUSED ON THE MIDDLE EAST. IF WAR BREAKS OUT THERE, IT WON'T BE THE END OF THE WORLD, LIKE SO MANY PEOPLE BELIEVE. IT WILL BE BAD, BUT IT WON'T BE THERMONUCLEAR.

When pressed further about this stance, the President actually demurred and brought up an entirely unrelated situation of concern:

DO YOU KNOW WHAT I DO WORRY ABOUT? KASHMIR. INDIA AND PAKISTAN—TWO NUCLEAR ARMED NATIONS THAT HATE EACH OTHER—ARE CONSTANTLY FIGHTING OVER WHO CONTROLS SLIVERS OF THAT LAND. AND THEY ARE NOT ALONE, AS CHINA ALSO CLAIMS PART OF THE MOUNTAINOUS

REGION! SO HERE WE HAVE THREE NUCLEAR ARMED NATIONS THAT ARE TRIGGER HAPPY AND FIGHTING OVER A TERRITORY THAT WANTS NOTHING TO DO WITH ANY OF THEM. THAT, I'M AFRAID, IS REALLY THE MOST DANGEROUS SETTING ON EARTH.

This little slip may have actually confirmed a rumor about the President's long-term plans for dealing with nations low on the "Freedom Index".

IS A CIVIL WAR BREAKING OUT IN CHINA UNDER THE PRESIDENT'S DIRECTION?

As is well-known at this point, the President appears to want to keep the United States out of being directly involved militarily with nations around the world. However, that does not mean the administration is keeping its hands completely out of affairs abroad. From the now infamous *Women's History Month* speech, it is quite clear that the President is staying well versed in the current political climate elsewhere in the world. Similarly, sources in the White House have revealed the President is in regular contact with leaders and opposition members worldwide, offering advice, direction, and assurances.

Yet, more so, while the President has no qualms about recalling armed forces, clandestine ones are another story entirely. While not as well-covered as *The Ten Pronouncements*, the President has signed a slew of seemingly minor Executive Orders. Among them were a set of instructions for the *Superintendent of Safety and Security* to increase and streamline information sharing between all investigative, undercover, and secret agencies—such as the CIA, FBI, and NSA, among others—so that they would work in concert. This suggests that while direct intervention may be on the decline, covert activities could be on the rise.

Which brings us back to what the President might have accidently verified. Recently, there have been a spate of seemingly unrelated attacks against government institutions and military installations in China. The only thing they have in common is that they have originated from areas that China is occupying by force—notably Hong Kong, Macau, Tibet, Ladakh, and among the Uyghurs in the region now known as Xinjiang. It has been an unsolved mystery where these insurrectionists are even getting their arms from and how they seem to be coordinated in their actions. It is almost as if someone is managing disparate groups centrally in order to disrupt China, keeping it distracted with internal matters so that it cannot be involved with external ones.

Why would the President of the United States be suspected of being the leader of this underground uprising? Because in a resurfaced interview from years ago on a relatively unknown podcast, the then-future President told the hosts:

 SOMETIMES, UNFORTUNATELY, WE NEED WAR. BUT WHICH ONES DO WE NEED, AND HOW DO WE CONDUCT THEM? GETTING DIRECTLY INVOLVED IS NOT THE SOLUTION, BUT PERHAPS WE CAN HELP FROM BEHIND THE CURTAIN.

Later on in the same interview, the one-day Commander-in-Chief expounded further. Specifically, the person now sitting in the oval office presented a plan that could only be described as self-serving manipulation:

> SENDING OUR TROOPS IN TO SETTLE DISPUTES RESOLVES ABSOLUTELY NOTHING. IN VIETNAM, IRAQ, AND AFGHANISTAN, ALL WE DID WAS CAUSE CHAOS AND LEAVE. AND WHEN WE EXITED, THOSE COUNTRIES JUST FELL AGAIN TO SOME REVITALIZED TOTALITARIAN DICTATOR; REALLY, WHOEVER WAS THE MOST ORGANIZED. THE ONLY WAY TO WIN IS FOR THE PEOPLE THERE TO RISE UP AND TAKE CONTROL FOR THEMSELVES. AND A CIVIL WAR—ESPECIALLY ONE ON MULTIPLE FRONTS—WOULD, AT THE VERY WORST FROM OUR PERSPECTIVE, TAKE AN UNFRIENDLY NATION OFF THE TABLE, WHICH ISN'T ACTUALLY TOO BAD OF A SITUATION TO BE IN.

Does this not sound exactly like what is happening in China right now? It is in the early stages, but if what is ongoing came out of the President's playbook from several years ago, then it fits together perfectly.

COULD THE QUIET IN THE MIDDLE EAST BE BECAUSE THE PRESIDENT IS PLANNING A SPRING REVOLUTION?

Interestingly, this is not the only instance where the administration may be meddling. It is no secret that the

President is a massive proponent of Kurdish independence, something that was made quite clear on the campaign trail. According to a "Facts Sheet" provided by the White House, the 30 million people that make up the unique Kurdish ethno-linguistic group—which is fourth in size in the Middle East after Arabs, Persians, and Turks—is among the largest societies in the whole world that do not have their own nation. Right now, the area that would make up an independent Kurdistan is split up between Türkiye, Iran, Iraq, and Syria. Strangely, though, since being elected, the President has been almost completely silent on the issue.

Syria and Iran were among the few countries listed as "enemies" in the President's categorization of foreign lands, but Iraq and Türkiye are technically allies—the latter notably as an equal partner in NATO. The relationship with Türkiye is already strained enough from the President's earlier acknowledgement of the Assyrian Genocide. Openly supporting a separatist movement within their borders would most likely be a bridge too far.

Balancing a relationship with Türkiye while also trying to support the Kurds has been difficult for many of the President's predecessors. For instance, during the rise of Daesh (ISIS) in the 2010s, Kurdish forces in Iraq and Syria became important allies, especially as they were one of the few military groups to make headway against the relentless assault of the caliphate. This was despite them being part of separatist groups that were not supposed to have their own armies! Yet in 2019 President Donald Trump withdrew his support and protections for the Kurds in Syria and allowed Türkiye to attack the area for perceived potential threats to their sovereignty. President Joe Biden tried to reverse some of this, but by late 2022 Türkiye seemed unconcerned by the lack of bite to the American President's bark and continued its extraterritorial onslaught.

So, could the current President be secretly working with Kurdish leaders across four different countries to plan something bigger? What makes this seem more plausible is the reverse of what is happening in China. The Kurds are not a united front and there are many divergent factions on how to proceed with self-determination. This runs the gamut from political assemblages that want nothing more than some semi-autonomy inside their host nations to the *Kurdistan Workers' Party* (PKK), an organization that is recognized as a terrorist group by the entire western world, including the United States.

When asked about the PKK in the past, the President was noted as saying:

 I CAN AGREE WITH A GROUP'S MESSAGE AND DESIRES WITHOUT SUPPORTING THEIR TACTICS.

Which brings us to today. The PKK has recently become very quiet. There have been no attacks in Türkiye or on its borders in several months, nor has the PKK put out any pronouncements or social media posts. The President of Türkiye has taken credit for this, saying that the country has finally been able to crack down and demoralize the collective.

However, what if this is just the calm before the storm? What if the President of the United States has been surreptitiously using the resources of the federal government to organize all of these disparate Kurdish factions across four countries together into a unified front? After all, the

President believes that only an uprising by the people directly involved can produce the desired results, and the President is a full-fledged supporter of a stand-alone Kurdistan. Would this not follow the White House's modus operandi exactly?

ARE THERE GOING TO BE RESCUE MISSIONS ACROSS THE GLOBE?

One area the President has been less discreet about is getting American prisoners out of hostile nations like Russia, Iran, North Korea, and Venezuela, among others. In public, the President has stated that this is a priority for the administration. Meanwhile, in private, the President has apparently convened several meetings in the War Room underneath the White House in order to get options to make this happen. From the few details that have leaked out about these sessions, the President has been portrayed as "gung-ho" about using any means possible to realize these jailbreaks.

Once again, though, the President seemed to prefer alternatives that involved covert missions instead of ones with direct frontal assaults. And to this day, it is not as if there has been a single mission carried out. As such, it is impossible to judge in these cases where things stand. Would the President really launch an unprovoked mission into a foreign land just to rescue one American citizen? The situation has not been fully tested.

And that is true of everything we have gone through here. What we have is a lot of rumors, conjecture, and possibilities, but nothing concrete. Somehow, with all that is going on around the world, the President's hands appear to be squeaky clean. But are they really? We can ask the questions here, but will anything stick? Or will it all continue to slide off the White House as if it is made of Teflon?

DESTINY IS A GOOD THING TO ACCEPT WHEN IT'S GOING YOUR WAY. WHEN IT ISN'T, DON'T CALL IT DESTINY; CALL IT INJUSTICE, TREACHERY, OR SIMPLE BAD LUCK.

FROM *GOD KNOWNS* BY JOSEPH HELLER

HOME, HOME ON THE RANGE

President's Speech at College Graduation Goes Far off the Rails

Students at Castleton University surprised to find themselves in the independent leader's crosshairs

Former Presidents Donald Trump and Barack Obama smile together on January 20, 2017. DOD PHOTO BY U.S. AIR FORCE STAFF SGT. MARI-ANIQUE SANTOS, Public Domain, via Wikimedia Commons.

May 28th (Castleton, VT) – When the undergraduate student union at Castleton University voted to have the President of the United States be their commencement speaker, no one seriously expected the invitation to be accepted and the leader of the free world to appear before them at their little-known small liberal arts college in the middle of the woods of Vermont.

But the soon-to-be-graduates were in for a seemingly delightful surprise when the White House unexpectedly accepted their proposal! The only hitch was that due to scheduling conflicts, the University would need to push out the date of the actual ceremony to accommodate the President. Given the prestige and attention such an event would give the campus, the University acquiesced. Of course, as with all things dealing with this Commander-in-Chief, what they expected to get and what the President intended to deliver were two totally different things.

While most people among the student body and the employees of the University were envisioning a rousing oration on their future potential and the opportunities available to them, the President wanted to talk about patriotism and tribalism—and specifically, getting over it. As the President said to the crowd:

 WE MUST NOT JUST APPROVE OR DISAPPROVE OF A PRESIDENT, A MEMBER OF CONGRESS, ANY POLITICIAN, OR REALLY ANY OTHER HUMAN BEING IN TOTALITY BASED UPON THEIR AFFILIATION. WE MUST INSTEAD NOT ONLY JUDGE EVERY PERSON INDIVIDUALLY, BUT ALSO EVALUATE EACH ONE OF THEIR UNIQUE ACTIONS ON ITS OWN MERITS.

After this, the President began to challenge the beliefs of the majority of the audience. Castleton University has a well-documented diversity program that has led to one of the most widely representative faculties in the entire country, especially in relation to women and minorities given the demographics of the area. However, the one place where there is a lack of breadth is in politics, notably that over 88% of the staff are members of the Democratic Party. This is far above the national average of 30%, and even the Vermont average of 57%. As such, it made the campus the perfect ground to contest the image of former-President Barack Obama being an icon of liberal ideals.

CURRENT PRESIDENT LAMBASTS OBAMA FOR NOT LIVING UP TO IMAGE

 THERE WAS A PRESIDENT WHO CAMPAIGNED ON "HOPE AND CHANGE". AND THUS, THE PEOPLE WHO VOTED FOR HIM DID JUST THAT, CHOOSING BASED ON THEIR OWN ENTHUSIASM. BUT THEY SHOULD HAVE LISTENED WITH THEIR EARS AND NOT THEIR DREAMS. THEY SHOULD HAVE PAID ATTENTION TO WHAT HE ACTUALLY SAID AND NOT WHAT THEY WISHED WOULD COME TO PASS.

These were the opening remarks the current occupant of the White House made regarding a former tenant named Barack Obama. President Obama is seen as a bastion of liberal principles, even shepherding through the *Affordable Care Act* (ACA) that ensured health insurance for all Americans, a program long pursued by liberals. He also oversaw the implementation of new policies like the *Deferred Action for Childhood Arrivals* (DACA) that protected people who were brought to this country as children from being deported. These were among a small handful of effective progressive actions that Obama undertook while sitting in the Oval Office.

Yet the person presently inhabiting that chair seemed to be inclined to break people out of the illusion that Obama was everything that progressive minds desired. For instance, on the campaign trail in 2007, then-Senator Obama was quite clear that he did not support marriage equality for LGBTQ+ people, but instead wanted a separate "strong civil union" that conferred similar rights. This piqued the modern President's ire:

 LGBTQ+ PEOPLE SHOULD NEVER HAVE VOTED FOR OBAMA! THEY HOPED THAT HE WOULD EVOLVE OR THAT HE WAS HIDING HIS TRUE FEELINGS TO GET VOTES FROM MIDDLE-AMERICA—AND MAYBE HE WAS. BUT THAT JUST MAKES HIM MORE DISINGENUOUS. YOU SHOULD VOTE FOR GROUPS AND INDIVIDUALS THAT SUPPORT YOU UNCONDITIONALLY. DO NOT EVER COMPROMISE AT THE BALLOT BOX; YOU HAVE THE REAL POWER THERE!

There were a number of other examples given—including anti-war activists because, while campaigning, Obama specifically said he would take troops out of Iraq and would redeploy them to Afghanistan. "He did not lie," the President noted, "as that is exactly what he did."

Similarly, the current leader of the United States invoked another one of Obama's less-than-flattering nicknames: "Deporter-in-Chief". Under Obama, more undocumented immigrants were removed from the country than seen in any other prior administration—both in terms of sheer volume and as a percentage of the total population. Efforts to entrap these people included creating "fake schools". Immigrants would often enroll in institutions that helped secure their green card status, at least for a limited period of time. Here, those people thought they were signing up for the same opportunity, only to find themselves being shipped out over the borders.

Finally, there was what the President considered the most egregious action by a predecessor—his response to being called a Muslim:

 OBAMA FOUGHT BACK AND SAID SOMETHING ALONG THE LINES OF, "NO, I'M NOT A MUSLIM, I'M A CHRISTIAN, I GO TO SUCH-AND-SUCH A CHURCH, I HAVE THESE BELIEFS, I'VE NEVER EVEN BEEN TO A MOSQUE." HE GAVE IN TO ISLAMOPHOBIA, HE SURRENDERED TO THE TERRORISTS. THE CORRECT ANSWER IS, "WHAT DOES MY RELIGION HAVE TO DO WITH THE JOB OF BEING PRESIDENT OF THE UNITED STATES? DO I HAVE THE SKILLS AND QUALIFICATIONS? CAN I DO THE WORK? MY PERSONAL CONVICTIONS HAVE NOTHING TO DO WITH MY CAPABILITIES, NOR SHOULD THEY."

According to the President, this was one of Obama's biggest failings and revealed a prejudice that many people did not want to and still refuse to admit was there.

President Believes in Listening to People You Hate, Even Trump

Deliberating along the same theme, the President said that we should also consider listening to people we vehemently are opposed to or thoroughly despise. This brought the conversation around to former-President Donald Trump, whose very name brought a round of "boos" from the audience. Said the President:

 WHILE HIS METHODS MAY HAVE LEFT MUCH TO BE DESIRED, PRESIDENT TRUMP DID PROPOSE SOME THINGS EXACTLY AS THE MOST PEACE-FOCUSED PEOPLE HERE WANTED. HE SPOKE OFTEN OF PULLING THE TROOPS OUT OF THE MIDDLE EAST, GETTING AWAY FROM THE NEVER-ENDING CONFLICTS IN PLACES LIKE AFGHANISTAN, IRAQ, SYRIA, AND MORE. YET IT WAS THE VERY SAME PROGRESSIVES WHO HAD BEEN BEGGING FOR YEARS TO MAKE THESE MOVES THAT BLOCKED THEM FROM COMING TO PASS.

The President then said that instead of fighting against President Trump, that the Democrats in control of Congress at the time should have worked with him to implement an appropriate, measured approach. It was a lost opportunity because they were more interested in being against Trump than being for their own principles. Continued the President:

IF THEY WERE IN AGREEMENT WITH THE POLICY, THEN WHAT WAS HOLDING IT BACK? IT SIMPLY WAS POLITICAL TEAM MAKING, TRIBALISM, MY T-SHIRT'S COLOR IS DIFFERENT THAN YOURS, I LIKE DONKEYS AND YOU LIKE ELEPHANTS! WE MUST HAVE CONVICTIONS AND NOT CHANGE OUR STANCE JUST BECAUSE THE OTHER SIDE HAPPENED TO SAY IT. YOU COULD HAVE DISAGREED WITH TRUMP 99% OF THE TIME, BUT YOU SHOULD HAVE SUPPORTED HIM IN THOSE 1% OF CASES WHERE YOUR INTERESTS OVERLAPPED.

PRESIDENT THINKS "DO NOTHING" IS A POTENTIAL VALID SOLUTION TO GLOBAL CLIMATE CHANGE

What this was all coming down to, the President asserted, was getting on the same page about "facts" and the need to build policy off of the same data.

As an example, the President highlighted that Global Climate Change is a real situation that is transpiring, and specifically has been happening more rapidly since the beginning of the industrial revolution, and even more so in the past century or more. "Denying climate change is ongoing," the President expounded, "does not resolve the problems created by it."

The independent leader of the nation then went on to highlight that the United States is the only country in the world where the right-wing denies Global Climate Change is happening at all. In other right-wing led governments like Hungary, Italy, Japan, and Australia, the regimes fully acknowledge the basic scientific facts. As the President explained to the crowd:

> Now, RECOGNIZING DOES NOT MEAN YOU HAVE TO AGREE WITH THE SOLUTIONS PRESENTED. YOU CAN BE HONEST AND SAY THAT ECONOMICS, STABILITY IN ENERGY CULTIVATION AND GRID MANAGEMENT, MAINTAINING HIGHER STANDARDS OF LIVING, AND PROTECTING HUMAN PRESENCE ARE MORE IMPORTANT FACTORS THAN THE ENVIRONMENT, OTHER NON-SAPIENT SPECIES, AND THE DAMAGE CAUSED BY SEA-LEVEL RISE. YOU CAN EVEN SAY YOU ARE NOT WORRIED ABOUT THE SECURITY DANGERS CREATED BY THIS, OR THAT YOU DO NOT CARE IF THE REST OF THE WORLD FACES POTABLE WATER INSECURITY.

The President also said that having this position should be respected, that we can disagree on policy, approach, and what is actually important; that everything was fair game for rigorous debate. As the President concluded:

> IF WE AGREE THAT GLOBAL CLIMATE CHANGE IS REAL AND HAPPENING AT A FASTER RATE THAN CAN BE EXPLAINED BY NATURALLY OCCURRING PROCESSES, WHAT ARE WE GOING TO DO ABOUT IT? A VALID

ANSWER IS NOTHING! WE CAN DO NOTH-
ING, DEAL WITH THE CONSEQUENCES, AND
ADAPT AS HUMANS DO. THAT'S NOT WHAT I
WOULD LIKE TO SEE DONE, BUT AT LEAST
THAT IS HONEST. DENYING THE FACTS IS
JUST MALICIOUS MANIPULATION IN ORDER
TO CREATE A PARTISANSHIP THAT WILL
SELFISHLY GIVE A POLITICAL PARTY AND
ITS MEMBERS THE TRAPPINGS OF POWER.

WHAT WAS THE PRESIDENT'S END-GOAL FOR HIJACKING A GRADUATION CEREMONY?

In what seems a common occurrence with this administration, the President wrapped up the speech and left the crowd perplexed. A smattering of applause could be heard throughout the crowd, but the energy that was there at the onset had long since dissipated. So that leaves one question: why did the President choose this venue to give this particular discourse?

It actually seems like this was a message more for Congress than it was for the students. Back at the *State of the Union* in February, for instance, the President presented a five-part plan to address the world's environmental concerns. But since then, Congress has made little headway in actually crafting legislation around the White House's chief concerns, let alone something that would be acceptable to both major Political Parties. Even at that time, the President tried to create common ground between disparate ideologies, but unfortunately it does not appear that approach has borne much fruit.

Although the Constitutional Amendments that removed the Electoral College and created a ranked voting system for the President allowed the first independent to ascend to the White House, the President remains alone against the hyper-partisan Democrats and Republicans. On the one hand, the President may be trying to soften up Congress in order to move the administration's agenda along. On the other hand, the President may be using this as a rallying cry to get more unaffiliated allies in the Capitol Building. If people stopped voting by Political Party and started going with their heart, it may ever so slightly break up the oligopoly of the two-Party system.

It should also be noted that in the books that inspired the Amendments that brought about the changes in the Executive Branch (**NEW & IMPROVED: THE UNITED STATES OF AMERICA** and **ALWAYS DIVIDED, NEVER UNITED**), there were also a number of similar recommendations for the Legislative Branch. Perhaps the President is hoping to create a comparable groundswell so that some Congress in the future will not be dominated by just the two. Regrettably for the President, barring a Constitutional Convention or a modification to the Amendment process, the Democrats and Republicans in Congress are not about to pass decrees that strip them of their own influence, clout, and control.

FOR JUNETEENTH, PRESIDENT SIGNS EXECUTIVE ORDER TO USE THE "BLACK TEST"

AN EXCLUSIVE, REVEALING INTERVIEW WITH THE PRESIDENT OF THE UNITED STATES

*A hybrid flag of gay and trans pride in solidarity with Black Lives Matter. Image and description by **EMERCADO2020, CC BY-SA 4.0**, via Wikimedia Commons.*

June 19th (Galveston, TX) – On June 19, 1865, *General Order No. 3* was posted around the town of Galveston, TX, saying in part:

THE PEOPLE OF TEXAS ARE INFORMED THAT, IN ACCORDANCE WITH A PROCLAMATION FROM THE EXECUTIVE OF THE UNITED STATES, ALL SLAVES ARE FREE. THIS

INVOLVES AN ABSOLUTE EQUALITY OF PER-
SONAL RIGHTS AND RIGHTS OF PROPERTY
BETWEEN FORMER MASTERS AND SLAVES,
AND THE CONNECTION HERETOFORE EXIST-
ING BETWEEN THEM BECOMES THAT
BETWEEN EMPLOYER AND HIRED LABOR.

While short (it only continues for another sentence), the announcement began the process of finally freeing the slaves in the State of Texas and eventually throughout the entire Union. This course culminated on December 6, 1865 with the ratification of the Thirteenth Amendment, which fully banned slavery and involuntary servitude within the United States of America.

However, just because slavery officially ended, it did not mean discrimination was over. People of color faced lawful mistreatment through segregation, Jim Crow laws, and other despicable undertakings. While the Civil Rights movement of the 1950s and 1960s would lead to official acts of bigotry being made unlawful; unofficially, intolerance, narrow-mindedness, and prejudice have been allowed to flourish. Slow progress has certainly been made—even to the point of June 19th becoming an official federal holiday in 2021 under President Joe Biden—but it is still far from a level playing field.

How can fairness, equality, and equivalent opportunity be reached? Well, the President of the United States was in town for Juneteenth festivities and took some time to sit down with our reporters to explain what the administration and the country can do better. And being this particular President, our team was the happy recipient of a new Executive Order! Below is a partial transcript of that conversation, edited for brevity, content, and relevance.

GCDN: Thank you so much for sitting down with us today, in celebration of Juneteenth.

POTUS: It's my pleasure, thanks for having me. I know it's not a Friday, but I felt it important to talk with people on this historic day in the place where it all started.

GCDN: Has your once-a-week press day been working out for you and the administration?

POTUS: Like anything, it has its plusses and minuses. I do believe it has made things a lot calmer around the White House, but unfortunately it has also resulted in the media having a lot more incorrect assumptions and suppositions.

GCDN: Does that include us?

POTUS: It includes everyone. But here you get to have the story directly from the horse's mouth, so please ask away!

GCDN: All right, let's jump right into it. June 19th is an important day in African American hist—

POTUS: I don't like that word.

GCDN: What word?

POTUS: African American.

GCDN: Excuse me?

POTUS: It puts the emphasis on the wrong noun.

GCDN: Would you prefer "black", "people of color", what?

POTUS: I would prefer "Americans of African Descent". This would place the American part first and foremost.

GCDN: Why do you think that's important?

POTUS: Because by placing a qualifier before American, it is setting people apart, making them "the other". It makes it easier to dismiss people when you do not consider them part of the same collective. And that collective is being American.

GCDN: So "America first", so to speak?

POTUS: Yes. The same thing for everyone else. Let's not have "Dominican Americans", "Japanese Americans", and "Italian Americans", but just Americans of Dominican, Japanese, and Italian descent. We're all Americans!

GCDN: This is not the first time you have gone after language as a precursor to policy. You did something similar with an Executive Order back in February when you removed "college" from all official communications and replaced it with "further education".

POTUS: Terminology is critical to how people think about things. Now that it is "further education", it can mean a lot more, especially for channeling resources into our badly depleted trades fields.

GCDN: So that is what you are trying to do here? Change thought processes with a modification of the terminology?

POTUS: It certainly would help! Let's look at a similar situation like with "gay marriage". Instead of calling it that, what if we said we were interested in protecting "human rights for homosexuals", of which marriage equality is one of them.

GCDN: What does this accomplish?

POTUS: It shifts the paradigm of the conversation. We are no longer talking about whether gay people should or should not have something. Instead, we are baselining it with the idea that there are these things we call "human rights". Why would you keep a human right from anyone just because of their sexuality, gender, or gender identity?

GCDN: You are making it about taking things away instead of granting?

POTUS: Exactly, we start with the assumption that all people are humans and are Americans and that gives them certain inalienable rights. From there, it is much more difficult for the other side to say why that right should be restricted for just that group.

GCDN: Is that enough to make a lasting change?

POTUS: It is a component of change, but it is certainly not enough. Direct action is needed.

GCDN: Through legislation?

POTUS: I would recommend that, but have no control or much influence over Congress. We already have a lot of other issues we are going back-and-forth about right now, so I don't want to push even more onto their plate.

GCDN: Through an Executive Order, then?

POTUS: Funny you should ask.

GCDN: You have a new Executive Order?

POTUS: I do. *{The President then pulled out a ream of papers from a nearby bag and handed over a copy to our reporters.}*

GCDN: This is a lot to go through.

POTUS: In legalese, it's necessary to be so verbose, but let me walk you through the highlights.

GCDN: Please do!

POTUS: The crux is that I am requiring all Executive agencies to use the "black test" when evaluating laws, rules, policies, and the like, and where the Executive Branch needs to fight back against the Legislative one, and even the States.

GCDN: What is this "black test" you speak of?

POTUS: It's a simple replacement mechanism. Let's look at a so-called religious liberty situation. Someone says, "I won't bake a cake for gay people because homosexuality is against my beliefs."

GCDN: Right, this is a real situation that has happened.

POTUS: Okay, let's do the replacement in that sentence. "I won't bake a cake for black people because being black is against my beliefs." How does that sound?

GCDN: It sounds racist.

POTUS: Exactly. Religious liberties do have limits; you should not be able to use your religion to discriminate against people. Yet that is exactly what Congress and the Supreme Court have allowed to happen. This mechanism provides a simple tool to tell if you have a legitimate religious objection or if you are simply being discriminatory and using your religion as a crutch to do so.

GCDN: Does this order require the Supreme Court and the lower courts to use this test?

POTUS: I can't order the Judicial Branch to do anything, it's outside of my purview. However, the order strongly suggests that they adopt the same logic.

GCDN: This is similar to your "Assessment of Harm"

from the State of the Union?

POTUS: Yes, but this is one level down from that. At the top we put people, but how do you split that when the parties are claiming equal harm? For one person it is their freedom of expression, for the other person their religious rights. Both are equally protected by the First Amendment.

GCDN: It is a tension that has never been fully resolved.

POTUS: And that is a flaw of the Constitution and the Amendments, but we'll have to put that aside for now. The bottom line is that this government has often put religious beliefs above all else, but there are dozens of other rights that have equal bearing in the Constitution and should be considered so. We need to reset the balance.

GCDN: Will you sign this right now?

POTUS: Sure, absolutely.

GCDN: Really?

POTUS: Watch me. {*The President then signed the Executive Order and handed it over before a member of the staff came to take it away.*} Everything in order?

GCDN: It certainly looks like it. This is quite an exclusive you've given us! Any other controversies you want to kick up?

POTUS: You want me to talk about Dan Patrick?

GCDN: The former Lieutenant Governor [of Texas]? He's been out of office for a while. What about him?

POTUS: I actually think about him quite a lot.

GCDN: Why is that?

POTUS: Well, back at the beginning of the COVID-19 Pandemic, he was very vocally out there.

GCDN: You're talking about his interview with Tucker Carlson on Fox News?

POTUS: Ah, you remember!

GCDN: What about that interview in particular?

POTUS: Well, I'm paraphrasing a bit here, but basically, he said that people who were high risk or older should volunteer to die in order to save the economy.

GCDN: That seems a fair summary, although he was mostly talking about himself. He was saying he was willing to die to save the economy.

POTUS: But that was the wrong thought process.

GCDN: What was the right one?

POTUS: It is not a question of whether you are willing to sacrifice yourself, it is a question of how many people you are willing to kill.

GCDN: What do you mean?

POTUS: Think back to that time, before vaccines, before treatments, before everything we have now to mitigate diseases like this. We knew nothing except people got it, they were contagious and infected others, and then some of the newly infected died.

GCDN: So, what you are asking is...?

POTUS: How many people are you personally willing to murder in order to save the economy? One, two, ten?

GCDN: And what if Dan Patrick or someone like him was comfortable with, as you describe it, murdering others for the sake of the economy? And what if that number is a lot higher, like hundreds, thousands, or millions?

POTUS: If they are comfortable putting the economy over human life, they are entitled to that belief. However, they have to accept they are advocating for preventable homicide.

GCDN: That is something you obviously have a problem with, right?

POTUS: Whether I do or not is besides the point; I'm simply laying out the facts. And fact is that if we take people like this at their word, then that means that they value the economy so much that they are willing to murder others to protect it.

GCDN: But is there a line where you would pass judgement?

POTUS: No, someone like Dan Patrick can only judge themselves. All they need to do is ask themselves, "How many murders is my threshold?" Simple as that.

GCDN: That's a pretty inflammatory allegation you are making there. Are you concerned about hearing from Dan Patrick?

POTUS: Not at all. I would be very interested in his answer. You see, it is very easy to deal with difficult issues that are life and death when the humanity part is in the abstract. It is very different when you have to think about people as individuals, with lives, hopes, and dreams.

GCDN: This is not about Dan Patrick, is it?

POTUS: You picked up on that, huh?

GCDN: This is about people being able to dehumanize others who aren't their same race, ethnicity, worldview, whatever else.

POTUS: All of that is a symptom of the same mindset. When you learn to devalue someone, you can devalue everyone.

GCDN: You're appropriating Star Trek again?

POTUS: Am I that transparent?

GCDN: The world has been following you very closely for a couple of years now. You do have themes and ideas that you repeat, even if you manage to catch us off guard with an Executive Order or two from time to time.

POTUS: Hmmm... perhaps I should shake things up a bit.

GCDN: What are you referring to?

POTUS: You'll have to wait and see. Thank you so much for having me today.

GCDN: We're done?

POTUS: For now, yes, thank you.

GCDN: Okay, thank you for speaking with us today. Our conversation has been quite illuminating, and thank you again for the exclusive Executive Order!

POTUS: My pleasure, as always.

ON THE EVE OF INDEPENDENCE DAY, PRESIDENT LEADS IMPROMPTU TOUR OF HOMELESS ENCAMPMENT

PRESIDENT VISITS THE TROUBLED PARTS OF WASHINGTON, D.C., TRYING TO BREAK LAWMAKERS OUT OF THEIR PROTECTIVE BUBBLES

A homeless tent encampment in front of Union Station at Columbus Circle in Washington D.C. on January 6, 2022. Photo and modified description by **ELVERT BARNES FROM SILVER SPRING MD, USA**, **CC BY-SA 2.0**, via Wikimedia Commons

July 3rd (Washington, D.C.) – On the eve of the country's birthday, the President of the United States grabbed several reporters, a camera team, a security detail, and anyone who happened to be in the hallways, and took them on a walk around the nation's capital.

Why it matters: The President has recently said that the federal government is too insulated from what is happening right outside their own door. According to the Commander-in-Chief, by staying inside the opulent halls of their buildings, those charged with representing the people have remained completely disconnected from them; that the marble-lined halls where everyone works blinds them to the suffering going on where they drive through every single day.

What happened: Visibly nervous Secret Service agents tried to stay ahead of the President as the leader-of-the-free-world guided a ragtag tour around the streets of the District of Columbia. This became especially true when the chief executive approached a homeless encampment and proceeded to interview several people about how they ended up in their current predicament, and what the government could do to assist them.

Between the lines: Although it was left unstated, the President appeared to be sending a message to the members of Congress about their insulation from the needs of average citizens, particularly those who have fallen between the cracks. Rhetorically, the President asked a member of the group from the White House, "What costs more? Killing someone thousands of miles away who might pose a threat to us in the future, or trying to help the people we have already failed at home?"

Zooming in: The President and Congress have been at loggerheads since day one, but it has become more pronounced lately as negotiations have recently fallen apart between the two sides over the budget. Here, the President appeared to be trying to strike a tone that set Congress up to be "uncaring" and "callous", as opposed to the administration that is literally out on the streets with down on their luck individuals. Should a government shutdown occur in October, the President could frame the issue as the fault of an indifferent and selfish Legislative Branch.

What's next: Most likely, the White House will continue to put pressure on Congress by controlling the message in the news cycle and presenting similar scenes. Any photos or videos of the members of Congress enjoying the Independence Day holiday in some semblance of opulence will be used against them by the media-savvy White House communications team. Such tactics have been par for the course for this administration, to varying degrees of success.

The bottom line: This move may actually backfire on the President as it could make it look like the head-of-state was willing to use desperate people as political props. However, reporters on the scene noted that the President appeared to display genuine empathy and did spend significant time with various people at the tent city.

▌ GO BEYOND

- *Budget negotiations are put "on hold" as both sides say they are too far apart to have constructive discussions*

- *House of Representatives creates committee to examine Executive spending*

- *Congressional leaders agree to meet with the White House following fiery State of the Union address*

PROTESTERS INVITED INSIDE THE WHITE HOUSE, FIGHT EACH OTHER INSTEAD

DID THE PRESIDENT REALLY WANT TO MEET WITH THE DEMONSTRATORS, OR WAS IT ALL A RUSE?

Protesters gather outside the gates in front of the White House. Photo by **KELLYBDC**, **CC BY 2.0**, *via Wikimedia Commons.*

August 7th (Washington, D.C.) – Protestors outside the White House yesterday found themselves the recipients of a unique proposition when the President of the United States invited them inside to discuss their concerns. Unfortunately for them, a lack of cohesion in the crowd made it appear that the opportunity would slip through their fingers. How this rare opportunity to meet with the President came about and the reverberations from the entire escapade has left the protestors, law enforcement officers, and members of the federal government reeling. Details are still emerging, but this is what we know so far.

DEMONSTRATORS A COMMON SIGHT OUTSIDE THE WHITE HOUSE

Gatherings at the barricades near 1600 Pennsylvania Avenue are hardly a unique occurrence. Since the early 20th century, those who wanted a "redress of grievances"—as guaranteed by the First Amendment—have chosen Lafayette Park on the north side of the White House as their preferred meeting spot. Notably, this has included people fighting for access to the ballot box, for civil rights, for and against wars, and in favor or disapproval of whomever was sitting in the Oval Office, amongst other causes. Over time, the number and reasonings for these rallies have grown exponentially to the point where there are hundreds of them a year, often with several on the same day. It is now at a point where most community organizers question the value of having a White House march when there is that level of noise to cut through.

True to form, it is difficult to say what all of the protests outside the White House yesterday were about. The President has caused no shortage of discord in almost every facet of domestic and international life, and this has created many fans and detractors. And as is normally seen, each of these groups also attracts counter-protestors, thus creating more bedlam and confusion around just what is being asked of the government, if anything at all. Oftentimes when protestors are interviewed at the gate, they are unable to articulate their own desires completely; much less provide a tangible and realistic solution.

A source inside the White House said the President was speaking with advisors in a tent outside the Oval Office near the South Lawn when some commotion became audibly noticeable. The President is known to prefer to spend time outdoors whenever possible and had a temporary "outdoor office" built so that work could take place there whenever the weather allowed. This has caused a lot of consternation among the Secret Service as it provides a location where the President can be regularly found that is also easily visible from outside the White House grounds. Moreover, many people who prefer their comings, goings, and interactions with the President to be less conspicuous have been annoyed when they have been spotted by the paparazzi and had their faces plastered all over the newsfeeds. Even other members of the President's own team have complained about having to leave the climate-controlled environment of the building proper (although it has been poorly rated by prior residents) in order to literally sweat it out with the Commander-in-Chief.

Whatever the specific noise was that reached the President, it apparently piqued the interest of the leader of the free world. One person who wishes to remain anonymous was in the tent-meeting at the time and said the President became increasingly distracted, and soon was unable to focus on the topics being discussed. Instead, the President asked everyone to hold on, got up, and started walking around the historic structures to see what was happening out front. Once the crowds were in sight, the President asked for a bullhorn, which was provided by an officer from the *Uniformed Division* that protects the White House.

At that point, the President began to walk towards the

fence and DEFCON-1 appeared to break out. Everyone in-volved with the head executive's security immediately jumped into action, trying to create protective corridors and bubbles, pleading that nothing untoward would hap-pen. A high-ranking member of the Secret Service even approached directly and attempted to dissuade the Presi-dent from proceeding with what was seemingly about to happen. Instead, the President literally brushed the agent aside and continued striding headlong towards the barrier that separates the White House from the rest of Washing-ton, D.C. and the world at large.

▌ AN OFFER IMPOSSIBLE TO REFUSE

As the President approached and people began to realize what was happening, an explosion of cheers and boos erupted in equal measure. Striding close to the fence, the President put the bullhorn to use and asked the crowd to quiet down for just a brief moment so that their concerns could be heard in order. If that request was the President's true intention, it only partially worked. For every person who stopped yelling, another one started screaming twice as loud. Finally, the President told those in attendance:

ALL RIGHT, ALL RIGHT, ENOUGH! I'M WILL-ING TO HEAR YOU OUT, BUT IT WON'T WORK LIKE THIS; THIS IS JUST ANARCHY! SO, HERE'S WHAT I CAN DO. IF YOU WILL ELECT FIVE REPRESENTATIVES FROM AMONG EVE-RYONE OUT THERE TO SUMMARIZE YOUR CONCERNS, THOSE INDIVIDUALS CAN COME INSIDE THE WHITE HOUSE AND PRESENT YOUR CASES TO ME.

This offer did actually silence the rowdy audience. Once that happened, the President thanked everyone and repeated the deal, saying they had up to two hours to make their decisions. The one caveat was that security would only admit them once all five representatives were selected. If they could not decide on all five, then no one would be able to come past the gates. With that pronouncement, the bullhorn was handed back to an officer and the President strode away to return to the administration's previously scheduled tasks.

It was at this point that the aforementioned breakdown began in earnest. There were at least a dozen different groups outside on the street at the time, and each one's key organizer felt they were the advocate who should go inside. Getting them to narrow down to just five representatives—especially given their disparate interests and opinions within those matters—looked to be impossible. Yet, some progress was made with an agreement reached about three of the representatives after the first hour and a half.

But with just another half hour remaining and two spots left to fill, the conversations began to devolve into heated exchanges, shouting matches, and recriminations. As the clock ticked away and the pressure rose, it was only a matter of time before someone physically pushed another person and a bit of a brawl broke out. After a short time, the *Uniformed Division* stepped into the fray and separated everyone, ending the violent outbreak.

While all this was occurring, the two-hour window expired. The three representatives that had been previously agreed upon insisted that they should still be allowed inside, but were rebuffed by security. Even the selected representatives' own compatriots fought against this idea as they felt that their specific interests were not going to be covered by those three alone. One of the preliminarily elected individuals had actually been lightly injured in the melee and was being attended to by EMTs on the scene. This bodily altercation seemed to have taken the wind out of their sails, anyway, and they did not object much as the officers recommended that they leave in peace while they could. Deflated, the crowd dispersed with some receiving medical attention and a few going to jail, at least for the day. The names and details of those detained have yet to be released.

WAS MAYHEM AND DISSOLUTION THE PRESIDENT'S TRUE GOAL?

With this being the outcome, the only question remaining is if this was an intentional manipulation to get the crowd to turn on itself, give up, and go away; or if the President truly would have met with the protestors. Either answer is fraught with questions, difficulties, and dangers of its own. Thus far, the White House has not responded to repeated requests for comment.

However, now that the President has made this offer once, other groups may take it as precedent and as an open invitation. Organizers now know that they can get the attention of the Commander-in-Chief just by being loud enough. If they have enough people show up with them, they may be able to gain an audience using similar tactics. If the leader of the free world was looking for some peace and quiet at work and at home, these actions may have just produced the opposite effect.

PRESIDENT VOWS TO PROTECT NAZIS WITH OWN LIFE

IN A SCINTILLATING ORATION DURING A STOP IN NEW HAMPSHIRE, THE PRESIDENT LAID OUT THE EXACT PRICE OF REMAINING THE LAND OF THE FREE

A painting entitled "The Battle of Bennington" by Don Troiani, courtesy of **THE NATIONAL GUARD**, *Public Domain, via Wikimedia Commons. The commander of the American forces, General John Stark, wrote in a letter declining an invitation to the 32nd anniversary of the clash due to his poor health, "Live Free Or Die; Death Is Not The Worst of Evils."*

August 26th (Nashua, NH) – Your rights, freedoms, and liberties are all under attack, according to the President of the United States. At a press conference held after meeting with the governor of New Hampshire ostensibly to discuss recent events in the State, the President addressed the media and others in attendance with a fiery speech about personal freedoms. Said the President:

> HERE IN NEW HAMPSHIRE, YOU HAVE A SAYING I VERY MUCH BELIEVE IN: "LIVE FREE OR DIE". IT IS NOT "LIVE FREE UNLESS THERE IS A POTENTIAL THREAT AND THEN BE WILLING TO TRADE IN THAT FREEDOM FOR SECURITY."

Not unexpectedly, after these opening remarks, the Commander-in-Chief then delved into well-trodden subjects for this administration including the contraction of military involvement around the world, the need to dramatically cut spending on armed forces, and the end of many measures that came about in the wake of the 9/11 terrorist attacks. From there, though, what started off with a discussion about the State's motto turned into a smorgasbord of different concerns related to the basic rights under the Constitution. As the subject matter turned to more domestic issues, the President seemed particularly concerned with how the country approaches free speech. Per the leader of the free world:

> I DESPISE NEO-NAZIS, THE KKK, AND OTHER HATE GROUPS LIKE THEM. BUT AS IS MY DUTY UNDER THE CONSTITUTION, I WILL DEFEND THEIR RIGHT TO FREE SPEECH WITH MY LIFE.

At this, the President went on to explain that the only way to get rid of horrible people is not by suppressing them, but by letting them talk freely and openly. This, the President contended, would allow "these idiots" to "prove how stupid they really are."

Scientific studies, though, do not back the President up in this assessment. Many times, results have found that just having exposure to these messages and ideas allows them to propagate, especially since the advent of the internet. This has been seen in many cases where people believe in complete nonsense despite the overwhelming evidence to the contrary. For example, look no further than the 2020 Presidential election where supporters of former-President Donald Trump were convinced that the vote had been "stolen" no matter the overwhelming amounts of verified and judicially-reviewed information that was available. This directly led to the January 6th attack on the U.S. Capitol Building by those very same supporters, and their denial after the attack that it either happened or involved their compatriots.

Still, the President also managed to stoke similar doubts, telling the crowd that surveys show that over 90% of Americans believe that the government or other organizations are trying to take their rights away. Speaking about this, the President said:

LET ME TELL YOU, YOU HAVE EVERY REASON TO FEAR THIS BEING TRUE, AND IT ISN'T JUST ABOUT FREE SPEECH. ARE THEY COMING FOR YOUR RIGHT TO BEAR ARMS? YES. DO THEY WANT TO TAKE AWAY YOUR RELIGIOUS FREEDOM? ABSOLUTELY. ARE THEY TRYING TO LIMIT EQUAL ACCESS TO JUSTICE AND RESOURCES, ESPECIALLY BASED ON MINORITY STATUS? YOU CAN GUARANTEE IT.

ARE THEY TRYING TO FORCE YOU TO BE
SOMEONE ELSE, SOMETHING ELSE, AND
CONTROL YOUR RIGHT TO LOVE WHOMEVER
YOU WANT? SADLY, THAT IS HAPPENING,
TOO.

We asked the President's Director of Communications to provide details on the data the President was referencing. They presented us with the results of many surveys, including a 2019 one from *Harris Poll / Purple Project*. While the results do generally align to the President's language, there are important caveats that must be highlighted. First off, there was no major agreement on what rights were being restricted. When forced to pick specific freedoms, the top five selections came in as:

- Speech (48%)
- Bear Arms (47%)
- Equal Justice (41%)
- Expression (37%)
- Religion (35%)

Thus, while it may be true that over 90% of Americans believe their liberties are under threat, there is no consensus on which ones. At most, less than half of people are concerned about any specific right.

Another example cited was the 2022 "Mood of the Nation Poll" by *The McCourtney Institute for Democracy*. In this study, on average 68% of respondents felt that over the next 10 years they would lose more freedoms than they would gain. This was in comparison to the remainder who either felt the opposite (11%) or did not see any change coming (21%). Unstructured responses to a question asking which rights they were most worried about losing aligned similarly to the *Harris Poll* from before, although the timing of the survey caused a large spike in concerns about "reproductive rights" and "women's health and bodily autonomy" due to it being conducted around the time of the Supreme Court decision in *Dobbs v. Jackson Women's Health,* which allowed individual States to ban abortions after 50 years of that right being guaranteed for all women.

Nonetheless, the President then went on to explain that various governments, political appointees, public servants, special interest groups, and individual people will always be pushing for their own agendas. The job of each and every person, expounded the chief executive, is to always push back as that is the only way to maintain a balance. Further, the President said:

IT IS THE RESPONSIBILITY OF THE PEOPLE TO PROTECT THEIR RIGHTS, EVEN IF OTHERS THINK THEY HAVE GONE TOO FAR. THAT IS WHAT IT MEANS TO "LIVE FREE OR DIE".

That may be a dangerous call to arms in this tinderbox of a nation. But as the President pointed out, it was inaction and complacency during the decades that *Roe v. Wade* was on the books that made people assume their rights to personal health decisions—especially those related to abortions—were protected. Because they thought they had won, it gave the minority special interests groups the time they needed to eventually turn the tide, and thus the fight had to begin all over again.

YOU REMEMBER LESSON ABOUT BALANCE? ... LESSON NOT JUST KARATE ONLY. LESSON FOR WHOLE LIFE. WHOLE LIFE HAVE A BALANCE... EVERYTHING BE BETTER. UNDERSTAND?

MR. MIYAGI (NORIYUKI "PAT" MORITA)
THE KARATE KID, 1984

IMPENDING IMPEACHMENT

With Just Hours to Go, No Deal in Sight to Avoid Government Shutdown

The President continues to veto every resolution from Congress, and Congress cannot muster enough support to override that veto. What happens now?

A meeting of the House of Representatives Budget Committee. Photo by **Creator:Jimmy Panetta**, *Public Domain, via Wikimedia Commons.*

September 30th (Washington, D.C.) – *{Updated with the latest details as of 9:07pm ET}* Unless something drastic happens, we are a mere few hours away from the largest, and perhaps longest, government shutdown in United States history. The entire federal budget—all 12 appropriation bills—must be passed by midnight or every government program and service will come to a grinding halt, save for those that support critical infrastructure and security, are required by mandatory spending, or have some other way to temporarily continue to function. Nonetheless, even those essential workers who sustain these operations will only be showing up because they are compelled to do so by law; most will not be seeing a paycheck for their efforts. In order for them to be paid, not only does a budget need to be passed, but Congress must create separate legislation to compensate them for the time the government was shut down. Meanwhile, no elected or appointed official will be receiving their recompence, either, including the person at the center of this maelstrom: the President of the United States.

▎ How Did It Come to This?

The President has made it abundantly clear—especially since the State of the Union seven months ago—that the administration is looking for a radical shift in Congress's approach to the budget. Specifically, the President demanded that the entire budget be passed together in one omnibus package instead of in a piecemeal methodology through individual appropriations and continuing resolutions; that military expenditures be reduced by at least 25% this year alone; and that savings and revenues be found by expanding personal freedoms, most notably around the use of recreational drugs.

Since the President announced these requirements in February, the administration and members of Congress have met regularly to try to come to some type of understanding that could be passed by the majority of the legislature and get the President's signature. However, leaks from these sessions have shown that they became highly contentious and had to be broken off for days and weeks at a time in order to let cooler heads prevail. Even the working group participants from both sides had to be switched out in order to try to mitigate the personality clashes that had become a hallmark of the negotiations.

Throughout this process, Congress had tested the Executive Branch's resolve by first passing a continuing resolution for defense appropriations that would have maintained current spending levels through the end of the calendar year. As was promised by the President during the State of the Union, the resolution was vetoed without ever having been reviewed. Here, the President reminded the members of Congress that the administration would accept any continuing resolution, so long as it did not extend beyond September 30th. This almost led to a partial government shutdown at the end of April when the prior continuing resolution that funded the military was coming due, but at the last-minute Congress blinked during this dangerous game of chicken and approved a version that only extended funding through the end of the fiscal year.

Attempting a similar tactic, in June Congress tried to do the same with programs seemingly closer to the President's heart, including ones related to healthcare, climate, and education. Again, the President elected to veto the legislation because it extended funding too far into the future, and once more Congress was forced to retreat. As such, every bit of discretionary funding is coming to an end on September 30th, leaving thousands of pages of programs to go through and somehow reach a consensus that could be agreed upon by all of the various contingents.

Some have asked why Congress was unable to override the President's veto and pass these resolutions as they desired.

After all, it would only take a ⅔ʳᵈˢ majority in the House and Senate to avoid all of this. Well, this is where the President has been extremely successful in driving a wedge inside the Republican and Democratic Parties, not just between them as is normally seen.

Neither major Political Party holds enough seats in either chamber of Congress to pass any legislation based solely on affiliation. Even if both the House and Senate were controlled by a single Political Party—which they are not—they would have no luck using a "Budget Reconciliation" process. In the past, when the House, Senate, and the White House were in the hands of Democrats or Republicans, they used their power to make massive policy changes strictly along Party lines. In recent history, this has included such immense statutes as the *Inflation Reduction Act of 2022*, the *Tax Cuts and Job Act of 2017*, and the *Patient Protection and Affordable Care Act of 2010*. In each of these situations, the core rule-change that allowed them to pass was removing the super-majority of 60 out of 100 votes needed in the Senate.

Using this methodology would only require a simple majority in each chamber in order to get any legislation to pass. In other words, just 218 out of 435 Representatives from the House and 51 Senators (or 50 Senators plus a tie-breaking vote by the Vice President) would be needed to reach an agreement. At various points, Congress has had those numbers. In truth, they essentially have even more than that right now. That said, it would still require 290 Representatives and 67 Senators to override the President, and for that they are sorely lacking.

That is because the administration has been very successful at peeling various sub-groups within the Political Parties off of their core assemblages. At a high level, there are pragmatists in the Republican and Democratic Parties that work together to keep things on an even keel. Each Party, though, has their own outliers of various kinds that they have to deal with. When one caucus or the other was in the majority, they often had to kowtow to these extremists in order to count on their votes. Unfortunately for them, in many situations those groups have later gotten burned when the promises made to them could not be kept. This has caused the people in those circles to become very distrustful of their own Parties, and thus they have become less inclined to offer their votes in return for some future mythical return that most likely will never come to pass.

To date, in order to appease as many Congresspeople as possible, various versions of the budget have been attempted. There have been all Democratic ones that bowed to massive unsustainable increases in social spending; and there have been all Republican ones that have gutted community programs in their entirety and dropped tax rates in a way that would result in uncontrollable debt. The overindulgences seen in these drafts were required to get everyone in their own Parties on board and were intended to be starting points with the other Party in order to just get enough people over to their side by walking individual line-items backwards.

But that did not work because as soon as they attempted to compromise in one area to get the other Party's vote, they would then lose the same number of votes from a faction within their own group. Eventually, this led to the more moderate members of both major Parties coming together in order to formulate their own plan. While this amalgamation had been able to successfully collaborate and pass several versions of the Budget themselves, each one has been vetoed by the President. Despite perhaps being the most compromise-filled appropriations bill in several generations, it is not enough to satisfy the White House, and Congress still lacks the votes to override that veto in both chambers. Once again, whenever they have tried to change something to get another bloc of votes on board, it would also result in the working group losing supporters, even among the so-called centralists.

All of that has led to this moment when the majority of both chambers of Congress have a budget that they agree to, one that starts on September 30th and runs through the entire fiscal year, and one that is a noticeably different take on the federal government than seen in decades. Yet, they lack the $\frac{2}{3}^{rds}$ super-majority necessary to override the President's veto, and consequently we are stuck and heading towards a shutdown.

▌ WHAT IS THE HOLDUP?

So why is the President continuing to veto each one of these versions of the budget despite the widespread bipartisan agreement in Congress? For what reason does the President persist in turning down a clean bill that acknowledges many of the administration's key concerns and ideals? It all comes down to one thing: military spending. While the Legislative Branch has actually been quite good about working through the various components of revenue and spending it has oversight for, as well as meeting various desires of the administration, there are definitely areas where the two are far apart. That said, sources within the White House have confirmed that the President is willing to let many specific details slide for the time being in order to get over the hump.

However, the one issue where there is seemingly no potential for compromise is with spending related to the armed services. The earliest versions of the Budget kept expenses at prior-year levels and the most recent edition has gone so far as to find savings close to 10%. The President has made clear, though, that this is not nearly enough, and it must be increased to around 25%. Getting Republicans to agree to any reduction was nearly impossible, but a number of budget tricks were employed to keep enough of them on board for this round. Any further cuts will most definitely result in getting the entire Party to drop out of negotiations.

Meanwhile, even Democrats are reticent to make any additional cuts. While there certainly are radical members of the Party that would happily reduce military expenditures by 80% this year, others that live in more competitive districts are concerned about looking weak on defense. This makes them comparatively conservative when it comes to armed forces spending. Voting patterns in Congress over the decades have shown that military and defense spending has increased and deceased almost equally between the Political Parties, with neither one being the true "defense hawk" or "harbinger of peace". If anything, each is equally in the pocket of the military-industrial complex.

Considering all of these factors, then, the only thing that is holding up the Budget at this point is the President of the United States. Congress has a version they could pass which would be at the Commander-in-Chief's desk in the next hour, but it would be of no use. The President appears quite content to let the entire Federal Government shut down in order to enforce the administration's stance.

Interestingly enough, the very first override of a Presidential veto was also related to a military appropriations bill.

In 1845, then-President John Tyler objected to a bill associated with what we would now call the *Coast Guard*, but Congress overwhelming chose to disregard President Tyler's veto. That said, it took two months for Congress to undertake that action, and the bill was not one that would have caused a shutdown should it not have passed.

Throughout history and including the current President, the chief executive has used the veto power nearly 3,000 times. Of those, Congress has only successfully overridden that veto on about 5% of occasions. However, when looking just at appropriations bills like we are currently dealing with, prior to this standoff there were less than 90 times that the President vetoed the legislation. Congress, in turn, reversed that decision nearly 15% of time, three times higher than the average statute. Still, that means that 85% of the time Congress has not been able to supersede the President, and this occurrence looks no different.

The last time an appropriations veto was countermanded was under then-President Ronald Reagan in 1982, but that only extended funding for some specific agencies for a few weeks, hardly the potential level of damage we are dealing with now. To find a government shutdown that ended by overriding a Presidential veto, one must go back to 1976 under Gerald Ford. Just as with this standoff, the entire fiscal budget ended on September 30th without the President's signature. In spite of this, then-President Ford elected to only veto some of the appropriations, not the entire package as the current President has done. Congress also annulled the President's decision just a day later, but it took over a week for the funding to catch up. Despite this turn of events, prior to a 1981 opinion by then-Attorney General Benjamin Civiletti, a "funding gap" did not necessarily equate to the government partially or fully shutting down. In the real world, this "shutdown" had no practical effect as the agencies continued operating as if nothing had happened at all. Since that time, though, things have obviously been quite different.

WHAT WILL HAPPEN IN A TOTAL GOVERNMENT SHUTDOWN?

Should the clock strike midnight without an agreement and the President's signature, due to that 1981 opinion and subsequent court case confirmations, there are many parts of the federal government that will either be severely curtailed or closed in their entirety. Other parts will see no impact whatsoever, and a lot of that depends on how each specific agency and program is funded.

What is being discussed here is the "discretionary" part of the budget, the areas where Congress can make changes on an annual basis. Nonetheless, there is "mandatory" spending that in the past Congress put into law that must be funded no matter what. At the top of this list are payments for Social Security, Medicare, and Medicaid. As such, no person on retirement, disability, or a needs-based system will have to worry about not receiving checks from most of the social safety net programs that exist. Conversely, these departments will not be able to process new applications for any of their services. That means that not only can no one start receiving Social Security who does not already currently do so, but also that no one can even get a replacement Social Security card should they need one.

And not all social safety net programs are part of the mandatory funding tree. For instance, the *Supplemental*

Nutrition Assistance Program (SNAP)—colloquially known as "food stamps"—falls under the discretionary spending of the *Department of Agriculture* (USDA). Without funding, those who depend upon government-issued EBT cards to buy food will not have their account refilled next month. In preparation for this potential shutdown, the USDA has already added October's payment to the cards and charged it to the current fiscal year while they still have access to the money, a tactic the agency used in prior shutdowns. However, if no agreement is reached, there will be no release of funds on November 1st.

It should also be noted that per the President's non-binding reorganization of the Executive Branch, the USDA, and thus SNAP, is now part of the responsibilities of *Science, Technology, and Environment* and not *People and Society*. The President had previously expressed a desire to officially move the SNAP program out of the USDA and into an agency that would fall under *People and Society*, but no drafts of the budget to date nor any other legislation have made it so.

Meanwhile, though *Veterans Affairs* (VA) also falls under the discretionary bucket, all medical services and facilities are expected to remain open. The main service disruption will be much like with Social Security, where new enrollees will not be able to have their applications processed. Further, purported non-critical programs like vocational training will be suspended indefinitely.

Beyond these human-centric areas, there is also other mandatory spending that is not programmatically related. For instance, interest continues to accrue on the trillions of dollars of debt the United States government has accumulated. By law, that interest must continue to be paid and the United States cannot go into default. While not often thought of by the average citizen, should the country fail to service its debt and consequently go into default, the United States dollar would lose almost all of its value and a worldwide recession would ensue. There are very few people in the government who want this type of situation to happen, not even the liability-adverse President who in the past has indicated a willingness to raise the debt ceiling should the need arise.

When it comes to the financial situation, there are a number of concerns that must be addressed. First off, the banking agencies like the *Federal Reserve*, the *Federal Deposit Insurance Company* (FDIC), the *Consumer Financial Protection Bureau* (CFPB), and other similarly situated organizations are self-funded and therefore are in no danger of shutting down. All financial markets should continue normally, however the *Federal Trade Commission* (FTC) will be shut down and will not be able to pursue investigations and cases. Meanwhile, the *Securities and Exchange Commission* (SEC) will have emergency personnel to monitor markets and accept filings, but otherwise will also be similarly hamstrung. If anything, the shutdown will give those in the financial market more leeway with less government oversight than expected. Some may see this as an opportunity to pursue opportunities in a less-regulated environment.

Of note, the stock market has continued its overall consistent downward trajectory since the President was installed. In general, Wall Street does not like volatility, and this administration has certainly contributed significantly to that. The market losses, more difficult working conditions with international partners, the jitteriness of CEOs the country over, and signs of price inflation have all potentially led to a general economic downturn that may already be in progress. Thus, although the shutdown will not directly impact businesses, money flow, the markets, or any other economic area, its fallout could trigger a full recession. Some are claiming that we are already in a recession based upon the President's actions and that the leader of the free world must be held accountable for "intentionally destroying the greatest economy of the world."

One particular area where there might be an impact on people and businesses is in relation to loans. With the *Internal Revenue Service* (IRS), *Housing and Urban Development* (HUD), the *Small Business Administration* (SBA), and other agencies either completely or partially shuttered, getting loans processed may be slowed down or stopped entirely. Most new housing mortgages should see no impact aside from a longer wait time to be approved, but every other specialized program might not be able to function at all or will be on an exceedingly delayed schedule. This could cause free capital to be severely curtailed, lead to transaction interruptions, and contribute to a worsening macro-economic situation.

On the same subject, it is worth noting here that while the government is shut down it will be unable to collect fees and other charges. Coupling this with the overall economic impact will amount to billions of dollars lost each day. Then, when you add in lost productivity, the expected backpay for all employees when the government eventually reopens, and the funds necessary to catch up on all that was lost or postponed, then any closure will end up being far more expensive than what may be saved while the government is unavailable, and perhaps even more than the President is hoping to save in total if things go on for too long a time.

Outside of financial systems, there are a number of self-funded and quasi-government agencies that should continue to operate without any interruption. This includes the Post Office, so mail and packages will come on time (or as close as the Post Office has been able to muster in recent years). Similarly, Amtrak trains will be maintaining a normal schedule, although some specific track repairs may be delayed because they are financed with federal dollars.

Interestingly, train travel might be the better option as going by plane may become more precarious. Officially, air traffic controllers and *Transportation Security Administration* (TSA) agents are deemed essential and will be compelled to show up to work. Regrettably, during the 2018-2019 shutdown under then-President Donald Trump, after not being paid for a couple of weeks some of these people just stopped clocking in. This resulted in colossally long security lines around the country and even a temporary stoppage at LaGuardia Airport in New York.

Some places that people might travel to will be shut down, but it will hardly be noticeable. The *National Parks Service* (NPS)—using a model also developed during the 2018-2019 shutdown—will be leaving all outdoor parks and monuments open and available, but will not be providing any services. This means no bathrooms, concessions, or trash pickup, which all led to damages during the aforementioned forced closure. Indoor spaces like the Smithsonian Museums will be completely shuttered. In a statement to the media, the NPS asked us to remind patrons to be respectful of national landmarks and protected spaces, to take out everything they bring in with them, and to continue to report anything suspicious or untoward to a local police officer.

The idea of refuse, damage, and other issues creeping up brings forth the question of what type of support services will be available? The *Federal Emergency Management Agency* (FEMA) will continue providing assistance in ongoing missions, but it remains unclear what would happen if a new one were needed, such as another hurricane making landfall. Seemingly, the President could use existing emergency declaration authority to empower FEMA to respond, but once again there would be no money to pay employees. Other agencies like the *Food and Drug Administration* (FDA) and the *Environmental Protection Agency* (EPA) would cease their inspections and other activities, adding a level of risk to consumables, drinking water, the soil, and waste services. The *National Institute of Health* (NIH) and the *Centers for Disease Control* (CDC) would also suspend most of their programs, creating a massive hazard right at the beginning of the Influenza/Coronavirus season where the government will not be able to effectively respond.

Ironically, the United States military would actually function rather ordinarily, even continuing to pay soldiers and civilians. Because of how much money Congress has outlaid in the past, the military is sitting on billions of dollars in cash and can continue to fund themselves through February of next year, and perhaps longer if they curtail certain activities. As such, military readiness is feasibly the least at risk of all federal government programs and services.

IS THERE ANYTHING ELSE CONGRESS COULD DO TO STOP THIS?

Given that Congress is seemingly unable to find the votes necessary to override the President's veto and the latter is disinclined to even sign a one-day extension to continue negotiations, a shutdown now seems inevitable. Yet, there is one area in Congress where there is broad support: disdain for the President. Could getting rid of the President be the solution this country needs?

As the first independent leader of the nation, the President lacks any support from the Democrats and Republicans who make up almost all of the membership in Congress, as well as among the Party-loyal voters at large. It is fair to note that even prior to taking the Oath of Office, the President lacked a clear mandate from the people. The Constitutional Amendments that eliminated the Electoral College and created the direct universal voting system that mixed ranked and negative selections—a scheme inspired by the seminal books **NEW & IMPROVED: THE UNITED STATES OF AMERICA** and **ALWAYS DIVIDED, NEVER UNITED**—allowed this comparable political outsider to rise to power.

While the President indisputably received the highest number of "net points", that is not the same as being the "first choice". In that category, the Democratic candidate received 41%, the Republican candidate 38%, the current President 13%, and the remaining 8% was spread among a plethora of other candidates. It was the take-home combination of second plus third choice and negative votes for the Democratic and Republican candidates that allowed this relative unknown to assume the highest seat in the land. That made many people, especially the Party-faithful already in Congress, bristle at the idea of being dictated to by someone who was clearly not the top choice of most Americans.

The Commander-in-Chief has not been helpful in negating this impression since the onset. Even before assuming office, the President had taken an aggressive stand in almost all dealings with Congress. Coming in hot like this—including threatening to arrest members of Congress if they got out of line—has not made the administration any friends, allies, or even a partner who could help work as an intermediary. In reality, the actions of the White House have created quite a few enemies, not the least of which are the Speaker of the House and the Majority Leader of the Senate.

Since the *Ten Pronouncements* on Inauguration Day when the President went completely rogue with Executive Orders that put American people and interests around the globe at risk, there have been calls to remove the leader of the free world. At first, Congress seemed disinclined to entertain these ideas, and the cries for such radical action only came from the outermost reaches of each of the major Political Parties. Nonetheless, as time has gone on, the President has failed to gain favor with Congress and has only pushed the envelope further and further outward. A recent interaction with protesters outside the White House that ended in violence and arrests has created a lot of chatter about the fitness of the President to continue leading the nation, even among the more rank-and-file members of Congress.

Combing through public and off-the-record comments, it would appear that there is more than enough sentiment in the House of Representatives to impeach the President. The question is, is there an appetite to go through such a tumultuous trial while the government is shut down? And if there is, would the Senate actually convict?

Although former President Andrew Johnson was impeached in 1868, Bill Clinton in 1998, and Donald Trump in 2019 and 2021, none of them were convicted by the Senate, which requires a ⅔rds (67%) majority in order to remove them from office. The closest any case has ever gotten was with Donald Trump's second impeachment in which 57% voted guilty; and in Articles 2, 3, and 9 of Andrew Johnson's trial that tapped out at 65%. Getting over that threshold is an intentionally high bar. Of the 21 national-level impeachments that have happened in all of United States history, only eight ended with conviction, and all of those were against federal judges.

More so, what legitimate reason would the House of Representatives give to initiate proceedings? The only acceptable options from the Constitution are "Treason, Bribery, or other high Crimes and Misdemeanors." Has the President committed any of these?

Treason is the sole crime defined in the Constitution, but it is rather specifically "levying war against" the United States or providing "Aid and Comfort" to its enemies. Since the President literally defined a list of enemy nations, it would be nearly impossible to say the President was providing them anything remotely close to "Aid and Comfort". And although many of the President's actions have been questionable, uncomfortable, downright hazardous to Americans, and even perhaps against the will of the people, because they are what the White House believes is in the best interests of the nation, they would be considered part of the normal course of governing and would definitely not be seen the same as "levying war". No one could seriously argue this approach.

Similarly, bribery does not seem to be on the table as there have been no accusations against the President related to accepting money or gifts from anyone, much less to get something in return. As a matter of fact, the President has actively ramped up enforcement in mechanisms like the

Hatch Act that tries to keep federal officers and employees from using their position and resources for political activities. If anything, the President seems intent on removing as much impropriety—whether real or perceived—from the government as possible.

That leaves "high Crimes and Misdemeanors", a term that has never been fully defined or tested. Former Libertarian Party candidate Jon Roland of the self-styled *Constitution Society* claimed the origin of the phrase relates to the office of the person, not the acts committed. In other words, if the egregious action could only be committed by the person because of their position, then it would fall into this definition. This is hardly a universally agreed upon understanding, but it is not without precedent. In the *Federalist Papers*, Alexander Hamilton likened the phrase to "the abuse or violation of some public trust."

Most importantly, it is a question of if the President has violated the *Oath of Office*. Unlike every other similar affirmation, the President's is specifically written into the Constitution, and thus carries a significant weight. It states in part that the President swears (or affirms) to:

> ... FAITHFULLY EXECUTE THE OFFICE OF PRESIDENT OF THE UNITED STATES, AND WILL TO THE BEST OF MY ABILITY, PRESERVE, PROTECT AND DEFEND THE CONSTITUTION OF THE UNITED STATES.

Thus, the question simply becomes: has the President in the past eight months done something that violates this oath? Remember that by the proposed understanding, an infringement does not have to be related to an actual criminal law but must just fall within the confines of breaking the above statement. During the drafting of the Constitution, George Mason was the person most responsible for the aforementioned specific phrase being inserted into the impeachment clause expressly because it would allow a review of the chief executive on all other grounds, especially in relation to a poorly run administration. Founding Fathers from James Madison to Benjamin Franklin also agreed with these assessments and gave many examples in which in an impeachment may be necessary, and others where it would not apply.

Based upon recorded statements, political opinions were not something Congress could impeach the President over; but personal misconduct, neglect, failure to perform duties, usurpation, abuse of power, or otherwise "obnoxiously" using the office all fit the criteria. So that brings us back to today. Was shutting down Guantanamo Bay against the will of Congress an "usurpation"? Would unilaterally depleting the country's nuclear arsenal and deployment of troops around the world be a "failure to perform duties"? Was exposing the goings on at Area 51 without so much as warning Congress "neglectful"? Was dangling appropriated funding and terrorist designations over the heads of foreign leaders and nations an "abuse of power"? Could an interaction with protestors that resulted in violence be considered "personal misconduct"? And most of all, is refusing to accept Congress's power of the purse and fighting with them for your entire tenure just plain "obnoxious"?

Any of these and more are possibilities. The President has not left the well dry on all of the potential ways Congress could turn words and actions against the White House. When asked in the past about the potential of an impeachment, the President seemed not only unperturbed, but actually quite interested. Whether this was a tactic to defuse Congress from pursuing such a path or not remains an open question, but as stated by the President:

 I WOULD ACTUALLY WELCOME IT. I DON'T KNOW WHY IMPEACHMENT IS SUCH A RARE THING. MOST EMPLOYEES GET REVIEWED ON A REGULAR BASIS, SO SHOULDN'T I GET A PERFORMANCE EVALUATION FROM TIME TO TIME? MAYBE NOT AN IMPEACHMENT, BUT AT LEAST HAVING A REGULAR INQUIRY BEFORE CONGRESS COULD BE A GOOD THING FOR ME AND THE NATION.

Even if the votes are there, the only thing removing the President from office will do is put the Vice President into the Oval Office. While the Vice President is not a political outsider like the President and is seen as more reasonable, that does not mean it will result in a better outcome. The Vice President is a full-throttled supporter of the boss's agenda, and has made it clear that the current situation would be unfurling exactly the same should their roles be reversed. It would seem, then, that there would be no benefit at all if things remained as-is.

Given that, would Congress remove the President and Vice President simultaneously just to get their own way? By the existing law detailing the Presidential line of succession, the Speaker of the House of Representatives would be next up, followed by the President Pro Tempore of the Senate. Although the two are currently from different Political Parties, perhaps Republicans and Democrats would be more comfortable with one or the other in charge compared to the independents presently occupying the White House. Although they do not care for each other, there is at least a familiarity and respect for the nominal bureaucratic process.

Reservations about this possibility go back as far as the 2003 *Continuity of Government Commission*, which highlighted that a new Speaker of the House could be elected who in turn might then remove the President and make themselves the head-of-state at any time, thus perpetuating a continual cycle of commandeering the position. Studies done in 2009 and 2017 found similar issues and more, noting many other holes in the process.

It is actually unclear and completely untested what would happen if the President and Vice President became unavailable at once, or whether the leaders of each chamber of Congress even qualify to be the President since they do not originate from the Executive Branch. There have been a handful of occasions in the past where the Vice Presidency was vacant and thus the next person in line was technically set for succession if needed, but it has never come to pass where it was necessary to test the theory.

Perhaps, though, this experiment of eliminating the Electoral College and creating this radically new Presidential election system was just too much, too fast for this Congress, especially one dominated by the lifetime partisans of the Democratic and Republican Parties. Certainly, when they first passed these Amendments before sending them out to the States for ratification, they thought it would solidify their own positions; they simply did not foresee this potential situation. Perchance, it would have been better to make changes that affected the makeup of Congress first— as also detailed in the previously noted manuscripts—so that the Legislative Branch would not be so polarized against such an unassociated leader. Of course, asking Congress to do something that would be detrimental to themselves would be a tall order, to say the very least.

Still, because the Amendments did pass, this is the government, system, and reality we now live in now. Barring another set of Constitutional Amendments that are more palatable to Congress and Party-insiders, this methodology is how things will be going forward. With that in mind, impeachment and the removal of the President and Vice President after just 254 days in office may be a valid and logical response in order to create a stability in the federal government that so many people, most especially the average voter, truly crave.

WE CAN KNOW ONLY THAT WE KNOW NOTHING. AND THAT IS THE HIGHEST DEGREE OF HUMAN WISDOM.

FROM *WAR AND PEACE* BY LEO TOLSTOY

FALLOUT

A Few Last Things

Executive Orders

An earlier draft of this novel contained the original text of the Executive Orders at the end of each of the chapters. A few have been preserved here in order for you, the reader, to understand the President's unfiltered perspective and intentions.

Guantanamo Bay Shutdown

By the authority vested in me as President by the Constitution and the laws of the United States of America, and to ensure the justice of the United States is applied equally to all people and in all situations, it is hereby ordered as followed:

Section 1. *Transfer of Detained Individuals*

Within 45 days of the execution of this order, all detained individuals currently confined at Guantanamo Bay Detention Camp at the Guantanamo Bay Naval Base in Guantánamo Bay, Cuba—no matter their legal status—shall be transferred to a Federal Prison within the 48 States of the continental United States.

Section 2. *Trials for Detained Individuals*

(a) Once a detained individual has been transferred to a Federal Prison, specific charges shall be made by the Executive Branch such that the detained individual can be tried criminally. These charges shall

BE MADE WITHIN 24 HOURS OF ARRIVAL AT A FEDERAL
PRISON.

(b)   ONCE CHARGES HAVE BEEN MADE, THE DETAINED INDIVID-
        UAL SHALL HAVE A CRIMINAL TRIAL SCHEDULED TO START
        WITHIN 90 DAYS OF ARRIVING AT THAT FEDERAL PRISON.

(c)   THE DETAINED INDIVIDUAL SHALL ENJOY ALL THE RIGHTS
        AND PRIVILEGES OF ANY PRISONER WITHIN THE UNITED
        STATES FEDERAL PRISON SYSTEM, INCLUDING HAVING A
        PUBLIC DEFENDER ASSIGNED TO THE INDIVIDUAL IF THE
        DETAINED INDIVIDUAL CANNOT AFFORD ONE.

(d)   THE WARDEN OF THE FEDERAL PRISON TO WHICH THE
        DETAINED INDIVIDUAL HAS BEEN TRANSFERRED IS
        CHARGED WITH ENSURING THE SAFETY OF THE DETAINED
        INDIVIDUAL.

SECTION 3. *RESULTS OF THE TRIAL*

THE EXECUTIVE BRANCH OF THE UNITED STATES AND ALL ITS
AGENCIES SHALL ACCEPT THE RESULTS OF THE TRIAL OF THE DE-
TAINED INDIVIDUAL AND SHALL ACCEPT ANY RESULT AND
DEMANDS OF THE COURTS ARISING FROM THE TRIAL. THIS IN-
CLUDES GRANTING COMPLETE FREEDOM FOR THE DETAINED
INDIVIDUAL SHOULD THE COURTS ORDER SUCH.

SECTION 4. *WITHDRAWAL FROM GUANTANAMO BAY*

(a)   WITHIN 180 DAYS OF THE LAST DETAINED INDIVIDUAL
        BEING REMOVED FROM GUANTANAMO BAY DETENTION
        CAMP, ALL UNITED STATES PERSONNEL AND PROPERTY
        SHALL BE COMPLETELY REMOVED FROM GUANTANAMO BAY
        NAVAL BASE AND ANY AREA WITHIN OR AROUND
        GUANTANAMO BAY NAVAL BASE. ALL PERSONNEL AND

PROPERTY SHALL BE RETURNED TO THE UNITED STATES AND ITS TERRITORIES AS RECOGNIZED BY CONGRESS AND SHALL NOT BE ALLOWED TO BE TRANSFERRED TO ANY FOREIGN HOLDINGS.

(b) SHOULD ANY PROPERTY NOT BE ABLE TO BE REMOVED AND RETURNED TO THE UNITED STATES AND ITS TERRITORIES, THAT PROPERTY SHALL BE DESTROYED IN TOTALITY.

(c) ONCE ALL PERSONNEL AND PROPERTY HAVE BEEN REMOVED FROM GUANTANAMO BAY NAVAL BASE, THE LAND SHALL BE RETURNED TO THE SOVEREIGN NATION OF THE REPUBLIC OF CUBA.

ASSYRIAN GENOCIDE

BY THE AUTHORITY VESTED IN ME AS PRESIDENT BY THE CONSTITUTION AND THE LAWS OF THE UNITED STATES OF AMERICA, AND IN THE INTEREST OF MAKING SURE THE HISTORY OF ATROCITIES AGAINST ANY GROUP OF PEOPLE IS NOT REPEATED, IT IS HEREBY ORDERED AS FOLLOWED:

SECTION 1. OFFICIAL ACKNOWLEDGEMENT OF THE ASSYRIAN GENOCIDE

THE FEDERAL GOVERNMENT OF THE UNITED STATES OF AMERICA HEREBY RECOGNIZES THE SYSTEMATIC MASS MURDER AND FORCED EXPULSION OF AT LEAST 300,000 ETHNIC ASSYRIANS AT THE HANDS OF THE OTTOMAN EMPIRE AND PERSIAN EMPIRE IN THE TIMEFRAME FROM 1914 TO 1920—ALSO KNOWN AS THE SEYFO—AS A TRUE HISTORICAL FACT AND DEFINES IT AS A GENOCIDE.

SECTION 2. POLICY AND GUIDANCE

(a)   THE WORD "GENOCIDE" SHALL BE USED IN ALL OFFICIAL
      PUBLICATIONS WHEN DESCRIBING THE EVENTS DETAILED
      IN SECTION 1.

(b)   GUIDANCE ON THE RECOGNITION OF THE EVENTS DE-
      SCRIBED IN SECTION 1 SHALL FOLLOW AS WRITTEN IN
      HOUSE RESOLUTION 537 INTRODUCED ON AUGUST 2,
      2019. ANY PRIOR RESOLUTIONS PASSED BY CONGRESS
      ARE TO BE SUPERSEDED BY THE LATTER'S GUIDANCE AND
      ANY FUTURE SUBSEQUENT RESOLUTION.

SECTION 3. *ACKNOWLEDGEMENT BY OTHER ENTITIES*

(a)   THE UNITED STATES OF AMERICA ENCOURAGES ALL ENTI-
      TIES—WHETHER POLITICAL, GOVERNMENTAL, PRIVATE, OR
      OTHERWISE—TO MAKE THE SAME ACKNOWLEDGEMENTS
      AND FOLLOW THE GUIDANCE OF SECTION 1 AND SECTION
      2 OF THIS ORDER.

(b)   NO ENTITY SHALL BE PUNISHED, REFUSED SERVICES, OR
      BE OSTRACIZED FROM ENGAGING IN ACTIVITIES WITH AND
      IN THE FEDERAL GOVERNMENT OF THE UNITED STATES OF
      AMERICA FOR NOT FOLLOWING THE ACKNOWLEDGEMENTS
      AND GUIDELINES STATED IN SECTION 1 AND SECTION 2
      OF THIS ORDER. NOR SHALL ANY ENTITY BE PUNISHED, RE-
      FUSED SERVICES, OR OSTRACIZED FOR OPTING TO NOT
      WORK WITH OTHER ENTITIES THAT DO NOT FOLLOW THE
      GUIDANCE OF SECTION 1 AND SECTION 2 OF THIS ORDER.

(c)   NO MODERN NATIONS SHALL BE HELD ACCOUNTABLE FOR
      THE EVENTS DESCRIBED IN SECTION 1. THE OTTOMAN EM-
      PIRE AND PERSIAN EMPIRE—ENTITIES THAT NO LONGER
      EXISTS—ARE THE MAIN PERPETRATORS AND THE ONLY PAR-
      TIES THAT CAN BE HELD RESPONSIBLE.

APOLOGY TO NATIVE AMERICANS

BY THE AUTHORITY VESTED IN ME AS PRESIDENT BY THE CONSTITUTION AND THE LAWS OF THE UNITED STATES OF AMERICA, AND IN THE INTEREST OF HEALING ALL WOUNDS BETWEEN THE GOVERNMENTS OF THE UNITED STATES AND THE NATIVE PEOPLE THAT RESIDE WITHIN ITS BORDERS, IT IS HEREBY ORDERED AS FOLLOWED:

SECTION 1. *APOLOGY TO NATIVE PEOPLE*

IN ACCORDANCE WITH PUBLIC LAW 111-118, SECTION 8113, CLAUSE 6—WHICH BECAME LAW ON DECEMBER 19, 2009—THE PRESIDENT OF THE UNITED STATES OF AMERICA APOLOGIZES AND ACKNOWLEDGES "THE WRONGS OF THE UNITED STATES AGAINST INDIAN TRIBES IN THE HISTORY OF THE UNITED STATES IN ORDER TO BRING HEALING TO THIS LAND..."

SECTION 2. *IMPLEMENTATION OF THE LAW*

ALL RELEVANT FEDERAL AND STATE AGENCIES SHALL IMPLEMENT THE PUBLIC LAW DESCRIBED IN SECTION 1 AND DIRECT RESOURCES TO DO SO.

SECTION 3. *DISCLAIMER*

AS WITH THE PUBLIC LAW DESCRIBED IN SECTION 1, NOTHING IN THIS ORDER
(1) AUTHORIZES OR SUPPORTS ANY CLAIM AGAINST THE UNITED STATES; OR
(2) SERVES AS A SETTLEMENT OF ANY CLAIM AGAINST THE UNITED STATES.

SECTION 4. *COMMISSION ON NATIVE PEOPLE*

IN THE INTEREST OF RECONCILING WITH AND RESOLVING ALL OUTSTANDING CONCERNS WITH ALL INDIGENOUS PEOPLE, AS WELL AS INCORPORATING INDIGENOUS PEOPLE INTO ALL FACETS OF THE GOVERNMENT AND SOCIETY OF THE UNITED STATES OF AMERICA, A COMMISSION SHALL BE FORMED WITH REPRESENTATIVES OF THE FEDERAL GOVERNMENT OF THE UNITED STATES, REPRESENTATIVES OF INDIVIDUAL STATE AND TERRITORY GOVERNMENTS, AND REPRESENTATIVES OF THE MANY INDIGENOUS PEOPLES THAT SHALL RECOMMEND

(1) A PLAN TO IMPLEMENT ALL UNEXECUTED CLAUSES IN EXISTING TREATIES AND RECOMMENDATIONS FOR REPLACEMENTS FOR THOSE CLAUSES THAT CANNOT BE EXECUTED;

(2) A REALISTIC METHOD OF REPARATIONS, CLOSURE OF LAWSUITS, AND SETTLEMENT OF ALL OUTSTANDING CLAIMS AGAINST THE FEDERAL, STATE, AND TERRITORY GOVERNMENTS OF THE UNITED STATES OF AMERICA;

(3) A PATHWAY TO FULLY INCORPORATING NATIVE LANDS AND RESERVATIONS INTO THE UNITED STATES PROPER SUCH THAT THOSE LOCALES SHALL NO LONGER BE HELD APART AS SEPARATE NATIONS THAT ARE ACCOUNTABLE TO A DIFFERENT SET OF LAWS, EITHER BY BECOMING PART OF THE STATES AND TERRITORIES IN WHICH THEY RESIDE OR BY THE CREATION OF NEW STATES OR TERRITORIES;

(4) A FUNDING PROPOSAL TO TIE ALL MODERN INFRASTRUCTURE—INCLUDING FULL RUNNING WATER, PLUMBING, ELECTRICITY, HEALTH SERVICES, AND OTHER NEEDS—TO ALL NATIVE LANDS FROM EXISTING PRIVATE, STATE/TERRITORY, AND FEDERAL RESOURCES;

(5) A MULTI-GENERATIONAL STRATEGY TO IMPROVE THE HEALTH AND WELFARE OF NATIVE PEOPLE; AND ANY OTHER CONCERNS AS DETERMINED BY THE COMMISSION.

PRESIDENTIAL PLATFORM

In 1992, I lost the Presidential election to Bill Clinton... or it may have been that I was 10 years old and not legally allowed to run. Either way, here was my campaign speech:

Jonathan Prag   Grade 5
                        English

    Hello, my name is Jonathan Prag, and
I am running for the office of President of
the United States. I think I am a good candidate
because I can help the world. As a straight "A"
student I have many ideas to help the world.
With my kindness I should be able to
conference with leaders so there are no
wars. I can't promise anything, but I can
hope, try, and love.
    My main goal is the environment. We need
to clean up our world. Instead of nuclear
energy I will use solar energy. I have found
out how to make things hover so we won't
need wheels, we could float. It will be a lot
of work to do all this so that you have
more jobs.
    I will put more tax on the rich and
lower on the middle class. I would also make
buildings for poor people, for free. The school
system needs more money for books, desks,
rulers, lockers, and other things. There are many
other things I could do for this country. Help me
make a difference.

Jonathan Prag   Grade 5
                    English (2)

    There are so many bad things and
good things in the world. There are
things I can do to help but I can't
do them unless I am president. You
have heard all I have to say, for now.
Only you can choose who you want
for president so make it a good one. Elect
me, Jonathan Prag.

    A Jonathan, you sound like a
man who knows exactly what to do.
Your ideas are very good.

DEDICATIONS AND NOTES

After a nearly two-hour search, J.P. and Caroline Prag found their brick at Babson College. Photo by J.P. Prag on September 3, 2022.

First and foremost, I must give all my thanks to my amazing partner Caroline, who has continued to support me as I pursue my crazy dreams and ambitions. Here is to you succeeding in chasing down all of your own aspirations! I believe in you and, of course, I love you[3]!

Also, I would like to give a special shoutout to May Sennewald. Back in 2019, after reading an alpha draft of **NEW & IMPROVED: THE UNITED STATES OF AMERICA**, May wrote to me saying, "Reorganizing the government I found very long, too detailed, and hard to get through. Maybe [two] books instead of [one]?" She was right, and I ended up removing a plethora of material from that book with a plan to put it into this one. However, in the end, that material did not make it in this book either because this novel transformed into something else entirely. That said, the remnants from my original concept exist in the chapter **NEW PRESIDENT "CAN'T UNDERSTAND" GOVERNMENT**. Someday I'll find a use for that immense table on government expenditures...

Also worthy of praise is my team of fellow freelancers, especially my editor Jessica Schmidt and cover artist Xee Shan. While writing is a solitary activity and there are many things I can do on my own—particularly considering my background in the technical, research, and financial areas—there are some things that you just simply need other people for. I'm grateful to have found individuals I can trust and who have helped bring my visions to life, all while maintaining their own style and approach. We live in a wonderful world now where artists can support themselves without having to depend upon corporate hegemony.

And finally, thank you, dear reader, for giving this story a chance, for the wonderful review you are about to leave on your favorite website, and for posting your praise all over social media. Reviews and word-of-mouth are the primary ways independent authors like me get noticed, which results in more sales, which in turn allows me to eat. I do hope you want me to be able to eat!

A peregrine falcon admires its eggs on April 21, 2022 in this screenshot taken by J.P. Prag during a livestream provided by the Audubon Society of Rhode Island. HTTPS://ASRI.ORG/VIEW/PEREGRINE-CAM.HTML

OTHER WORKS

*PLEASE VISIT **www.jpprag.com** TO SEE ALL UPCOMING WORKS, PRIOR WORKS, GENERAL ARTICLES, AND CURRENT STATUS.*

RELATED PRIOR WORKS

NEW & IMPROVED: THE UNITED STATES OF AMERICA

NEW & IMPROVED – BOOK 1

Is there a way to save America and ensure justice and freedom for all? There is... if you are willing to rethink and rebuild the entire Constitution!

HTTPS://AMAZON.COM/DP/**B08FCPB5JN**

ALWAYS DIVIDED, NEVER UNITED: AND OTHER STORIES DURING A TIME OF PANDEMICS & POLITICS

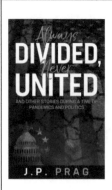

NEW & IMPROVED – BOOK 2

Have the troubles of our age ripped us apart more than any point in history? Or has it forever been this way?

HTTPS://AMAZON.COM/DP/**B09YDM25MB**

OTHER PRIOR WORKS

COMING SOON

Stay up to date at **WWW.JPPRAG.COM/UPCOMING**

COMPENDIUM OF HUMANITY'S END
Should humanity populate the stars and find no other life, what does that mean? What happens when those sent out to find life are met with nothing but constant failure?

AESTAS: THE YELLOW BALLOON
Venus is the true haven for humanity's expansion into the universe; but for some it is simply not enough.
Preview: ***HTTPS://WWW.JPPRAG.COM/POST/AESTAS-THE-YELLOW-BALLOON-VOCAL-NEW-WORLDS-CHALLENGE***

LOST RUMORS
You wake up to find several days of your life are missing. Do you trust everyone else's recollection of events, even if it doesn't line up with how you see yourself?

ABOUT THE AUTHOR

J.P. Prag is a Pisces, even though that does not mean anything. However, ten of the stars in Pisces are known to host planets, though these stars are nowhere near each other. One of the planets (GU Pisces b) takes around 80,000 Earth years to circle its sun. Of note, some of the stars are not stars at all, but are entire galaxies! Further scientific examination has discovered many other faint galaxies, nebulae, stars, and other stellar objects within the Pisces general area. A couple of those galaxies are on a collision course, so look out for that over the next several hundred million years or so.

When not observing the stars at the Ladd Observatory, J.P. Prag can be found several blocks away at his home and office in Providence, RI, U.S.A. with his partner Caroline and their many tall ferns and philodendrons, lazy lying down cacti, outside pet squirrels (including Squirrel the Raccoon), and a stuffed pet sloth named Peeve.

For more irreverent details (and perhaps some pertinent ones, too?) and contact information, please visit **WWW.JPPRAG.COM**.

VERSION HISTORY

Version Number	Version Date	Version Notes
0.00	2020-01-28	Draft Started
0.10	2020-04-15	Shell Outline Transfer Complete
1.00	2022-10-19	Alpha Draft
1.50	2022-11-04	Alpha Draft – Edited
2.00	2022-11-23	Beta Draft
2.50	2022-12-15	Beta Draft – Edited
3.00	2023-01-17	Final Release Form

COPYRIGHTS AND DISCLAIMERS

First Edition February 2023

Printed everywhere in the world on an on-demand basis from the nearest regional production and distribution center.

Edited by Jessica Schmidt
HTTPS://WWW.FIVERR.COM/CURIOUSWOMAN271

Cover art by Xee Shan
HTTPS://WWW.FIVERR.COM/XEE_DESIGNS1

ISBN 978-1-7353287-9-9 // eBook
ISBN 979-8-9874980-0-2 // Hardcover
ISBN 979-8-9874980-1-9 // Paperback

Basil Junction Publishing
7 Knowles Street
Providence, RI 02906

WWW.JPPRAG.COM

CPSIA information can be obtained
at www.ICGtesting.com
Printed in the USA
BVHW011942130223
658423BV00006B/44